MAD ABOUT THE MOVIES
DIRECTOR'S CUT

METRO BOOKS
NEW YORK

This 2008 edition published by Metro Books, by arrangement with MAD Books.

Jacket design by Sam Viviano

Metro Books
122 Fifth Avenue
New York, NY 10011

ISBN-13: 978-1-4351-1362-6

Printed and bound in the United States of America.

First edition
1 3 5 7 9 10 8 6 4 2

Visit MAD online at www.madmag.com

Though Alfred E. Neuman wasn't the first to say "A fool and his money are soon parted,"
here's your chance to prove that old adage right—subscribe to MAD!
Simply call 1-800-4-MADMAG and mention code 5MBN3.
Operators are standing by (the water cooler).

This book is dedicated to

Mort Drucker.

For more than 50 years he has demonstrated a keen eye,
brilliant craftsmanship, and unmatched wit illustrating *MAD* movie satires—
an art form he created.

CREDITS

Introduction by Roger Ebert

"Groan With the Wind" (*Gone With the Wind*) by Stan Hart, Illustrated by Jack Davis (*MAD* #300)

"Casabonkers" (*Casablanca*) by Arnie Kogen, illustrated by Mort Drucker (*MAD* #300)

"Blue-Eyed Kook" (*Cool Hand Luke*) by Stan Hart, illustrated by Mort Drucker (*MAD* #120)

"Balmy and Clod" (*Bonnie and Clyde*) by Larry Siegel, illustrated by Mort Drucker (*MAD* #119)

"Midnight Wowboy" (*Midnight Cowboy*) by Stan Hart, illustrated by Mort Drucker (*MAD* #134)

"The $ound of Money" (*The Sound of Music*) by Stan Hart, illustrated by Mort Drucker (*MAD* #108)

"A Crockwork Lemon" (*A Clockwork Orange*) by Stan Hart, illustrated by George Woodbridge (*MAD* #159)

"What's the Connection" (*The French Connection*) by Dick DeBartolo, illustrated by Mort Drucker (*MAD* #325)

"Put*On" (*Patton*) by Larry Siegel, illustrated by Mort Drucker (*MAD* #140)

"M*I*S*H M*O*S*H" (*M*A*S*H*) by Arnie Kogen, illustrated by Angelo Torres (*MAD* #138)

"The Oddfather" (*The Godfather*) by Larry Siegel, illustrated by Mort Drucker (*MAD* #155)

"Cliché Movie Script: The 'Opera' Movie" by Harry Purvis, illustrated by Bruce Stark (*MAD* #126)

"Who in the Heck Is Virginia Woolfe?" (*Who's Afraid of Virginia Woolf?*)
by Larry Siegel, illustrated by Mort Drucker (*MAD* #109)

"Dirty Larry" (*Dirty Harry*) by Arnie Kogen, illustrated by Mort Drucker (*MAD* #153)

"Scenes We'd Like to See: The Cops Close In" by Klaus Nordling, illustrated by Mort Drucker (*MAD* #49)

"The Zing" (*The Sting*) by Arnie Kogen, illustrated by Mort Drucker (*MAD* #171)

"The Odd Father Part, Too!" (*The Godfather, Part II*) by Larry Siegel, illustrated by Mort Drucker (*MAD* #178)

"Chinaclown" (*Chinatown*) by Larry Siegel, illustrated by Mort Drucker (*MAD* #173)

"Billy Jock" (*Billy Jack*) by Stan Hart, illustrated by Angelo Torres (*MAD* #168)

"The Towering Sterno" (*The Towering Inferno*) by Dick DeBartolo, illustrated by Mort Drucker (*MAD* #177)

"Assaulted State" (*Altered States*) by Dick DeBartolo, illustrated by Angelo Torres (*MAD* #225)

"Dum-Dum Afternoon" (*Dog Day Afternoon*) by Larry Siegel, illustrated by Mort Drucker (*MAD* #183)

"Scenes We'd Like to See: Driving the Golden Spike"
by Eugene St. Jean, illustrated by George Wodbridge (*MAD* #51)

"The Stooge-itive" (*The Fugitive*) by Dick DeBartolo, illustrated by Angelo Torres (*MAD* #325)

"A Crock O' (Blip!) Now" (*Apocalypse Now*) by Larry Siegel, illustrated by Mort Drucker (*MAD* #215)

"Scenes We'd Like to See: The Human Shield" by Joe Orlando (*MAD* #36)

"A Few Goofy Men" (*A Few Good Men*) by Dick DeBartolo, illustrated by Mort Drucker (*MAD* #320)

"Scenes We'd Like to See: The Big Break" by Gary Belkin, illustrated by Joe Orlando (*MAD* #50)

"The Shiner" (*The Shining*) by Larry Siegel, illustrated by Angelo Torres (*MAD* #221)

"Scenes We'd Like to See: The Doctor's Pronouncement" by Al Jaffee, illustrated by Mort Drucker (*MAD* #64)

"Bullbit" (*Bullitt*) by Al Jaffee, illustrated by Mort Drucker (*MAD* #127)

"Mavershtick" (*Maverick*) by Arnie Kogen, illustrated by Mort Ducker (*MAD* #331)

"Twit-sters" (*Twister*) by Arnie Kogen, illustrated by Paul Coker (*MAD* #349)

"Raving Bully" (*Raging Bull*) by Larry Siegel, illustrated by Mort Drucker (*MAD* #224)

"Scenes We'd Like to See: The Race to the Crossing" by Gary Belkin, illustrated by George Woodbridge (*MAD* #57)

"Marred Attack!" (*Mars Attacks!*) by Stan Hart, illustrated by Angelo Torres (*MAD* #353)

"Corntact" (*Contact*) by Dick DeBartolo, illustrated by Sam Viviano (*MAD* #363)

"Traff-Eccch!" (*Traffic*) by Arnie Kogen, illustrated by Tom Richmond (*MAD* #405)

"Planet of the Remakes" (*Planet of the Apes*) by Dick DeBartolo, illustrated by Ray Alma (*MAD* #411)

(continued on last page of book)

INTRODUCTION

I **LEARNED TO BE A MOVIE CRITIC BY READING** *MAD* **MAGAZINE.** I learned a lot of other things from the magazine too, including a whole new slant on society. *MAD* supplied the first ironic humor to appear in my life. One day I was a trusting, credulous youth who approached the Princess Theater with pennies and nickels grasped in my sweaty palm, eager to see the latest matinee adventures of my heroes Lash La Rue and Whip Wilson. The next day I was a *MAD* reader, and could look down with scorn upon my classmates who sat goggle-eyed through clichés and stereotypes.

MAD's parodies made me aware of the machine inside the skin—of the way a movie might look original on the outside, while inside it was just recycling the same dumb old formulas. I did not read the magazine, I plundered it for clues to the universe. Studying each issue carefully, I learned about standard dialogue and obligatory scenes, cardboard characters and giant gaps in plausibility, and "Scenes We'd Like to See." Pauline Kael lost it at the movies; I lost it at *MAD* Magazine.

Today's moviegoers are surrounded by a sea of cynical media. It was more innocent in the far-off days of my youth in downstate Illinois. It was in *MAD* Magazine, for example, that I was first exposed to the very notion of a foreign-language film. I thought all movies were in English. After all, everyone I knew spoke English, didn't they? And had I ever seen a subtitled film? Certainly not. I knew theoretically that in places like France they spoke another language—but even there I figured they had to understand at least enough English to go to the movies.

MAD ended my illusions with an article satirizing inaccurately translated subtitles. A hooker under a street lamp made proposals that looked steamy in the drawings but were completely innocent in the subtitles. Come to think of it, that might also have been the first place where I learned about hookers. In my bucolic hometown, surrounded by waving fields of soybeans, the only people who stood under street lamps were waiting for the bus.

MAD's parodies not only destroyed my innocence, they also helped to demythologize the Hollywood movie star. When *MAD* was born, people still took stars seriously. They were treated like gods, or royalty. People actually asked them to sign scraps of paper! Within a few years *MAD* had so completely warped the national value system that matinee idols were laughingstocks, and the only actors who could get work looked like extras from a Dickens novel. Tab Hunter was out, Anthony Perkins was in, and *MAD* gets the credit.

My only regret is that more moviegoers don't learn from *MAD*'s movie parodies. Study this book and never again be taken in by *Mars Attacks! MAD* and its influence have simply made some kinds of movies impossible. *Scream* and *Scream 2*, for example, are a tribute to *MAD*: horror movies have started making fun of themselves as a preventive measure.

The proof that *MAD* has good taste in movies is that, generally speaking, the magazine hasn't satirized bad ones. This volume targets such films as *Who's Afraid of Virginia Woolf?* and *Bonnie and Clyde*. Pretty good choices. I love the whole *fershlugginer* thing. Congratulations to the Usual Gang of Idiots.

—Roger Ebert

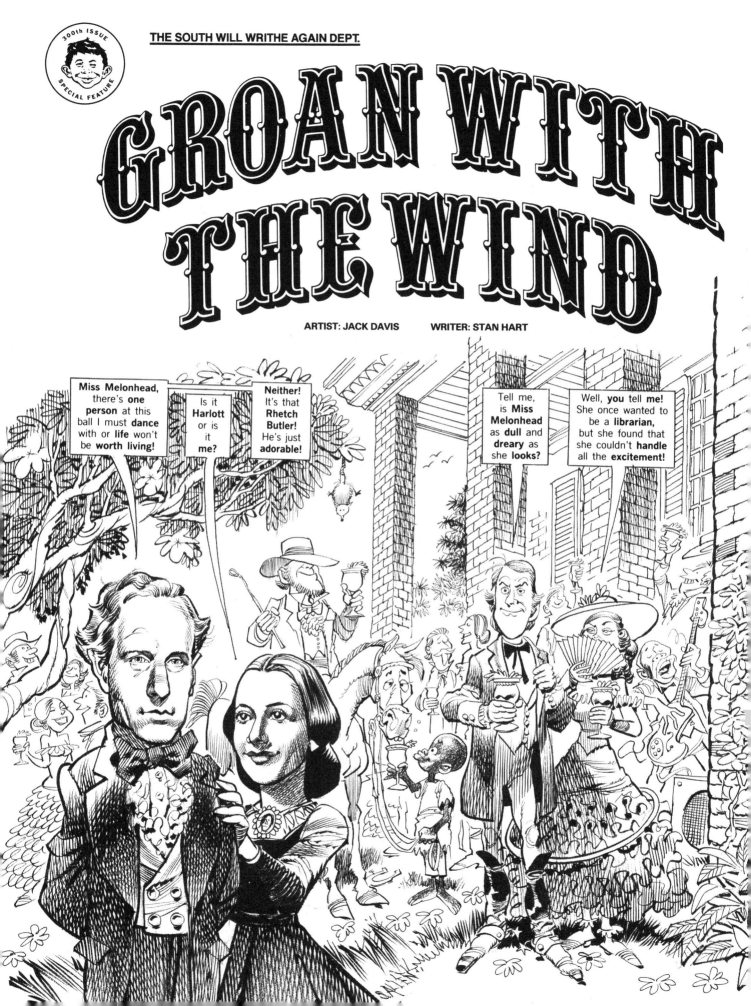

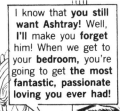

SABONKERS

ARTIST: MORT DRUCKER WRITER: ARNIE KOGEN

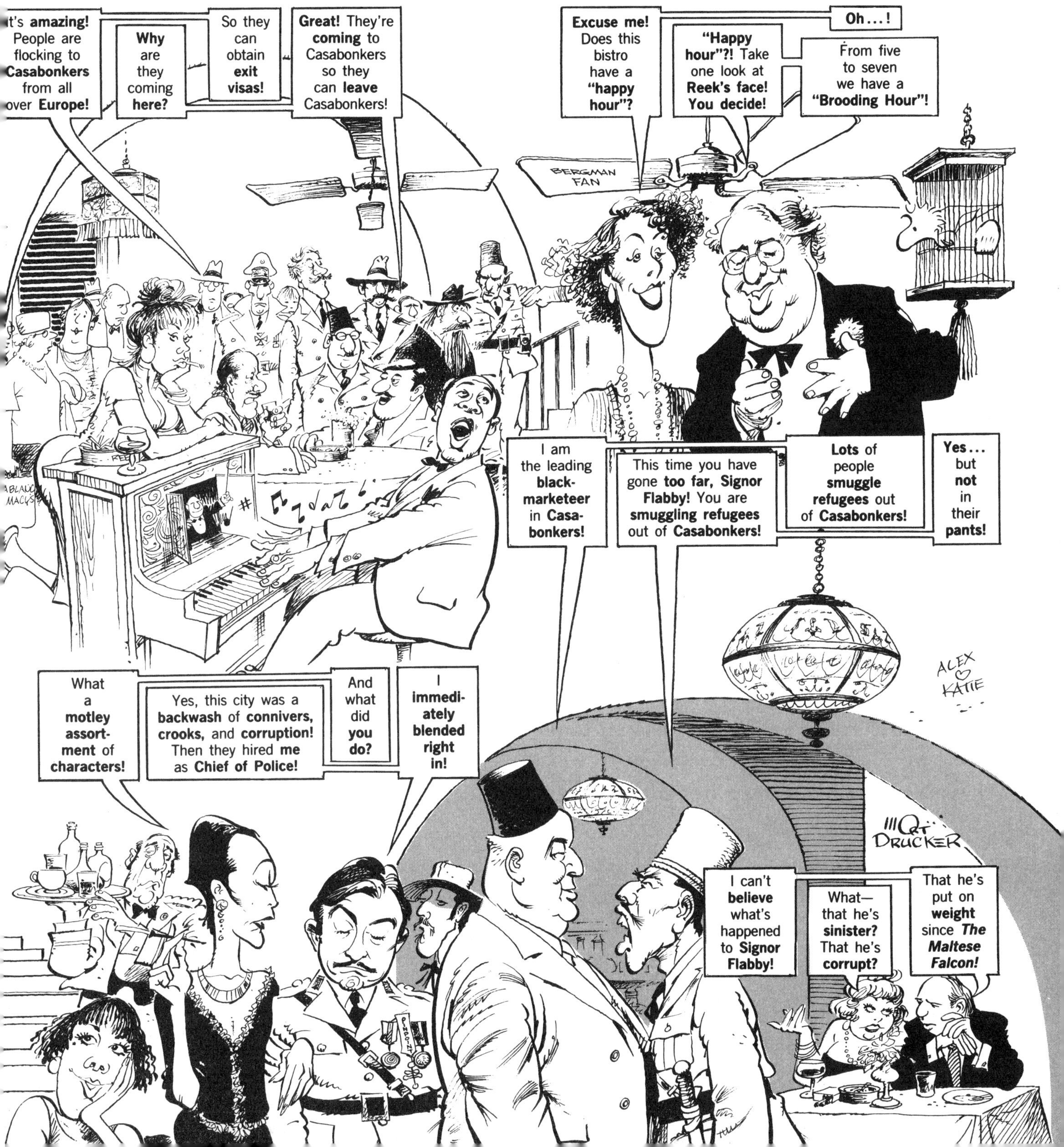

ESCAPE-GOAT DEPT.

Years ago, when they made a prison picture, you knew exactly what was going on. The guards were all sadistic and the prisoners were all regular guys under their tough exteriors. But today, things are different. Today,

I get **green** gum balls! I get **purple** gum balls! I get **white** gum balls! But **never** . . . never **once** in my **whole life** have I ever gotten a **marbleized gum ball**! So I'm smashin' every gum ball machine in this town until **I get** a marbleized gum ball!

Sorry, son, but marbleized gum balls are **strictly reserved** for members of **"The Establishment"**! And those gum ball machines **belong** to "The Establishment"! So you're **under arrest** for **trying to smash "The Establishment"**!

Okay! You can arrest me! But I'm lettin' you know now that even though I **failed** to smash "The Establishment", I'm **not** gonna let "The Establishment" **smash ME**! Not . . .

BLU

All right, now we're gonna get along jus' fine if you always do **exactly as I say**, no matter **how unreasonable** . . . an' if you always **treat me with tremendous respect**, no matter **how nasty** I get . . . an' if you always remember that you have **absolutely no rights**, no matter **how miserable** I make your life!

In **other words**, being **here** will be just like living at **home** with our parents!

That's **right**, smart guy! Okay—what's your name?

Kook Jerkson!

So **you're** Jerkson! I hear that some folks consider you to be a **hero**! Just what did you **do**?

I burned my **Draft Card**!

Well, **THAT** was an idle gesture . . . especially since you were in **Vietnam** at the time!

HE DIDN'T LISTEN

a prison picture isn't really about prison and prisoners. Today, it's all symbolism, and you have to figure out what's going on. Like f'rinstance in this MAD version of a recent prison picture that begins like this:

E-EYED KOOK

ARTIST: MORT DRUCKER WRITER: STAN HART

If you **don't make your bed**, you go **in the box**! If you **talk back**, you go **in the box**! If you **forget your number**, you go **in the box**! If you're **late**, you go **in the box**!

Who does he think he **is**!?

Señor Wences!

All right, **everybody outside**! Here's the **schedule** for today! **Stagline**, you get busy on your **raffia**! **Society Head**, you finish up your **wallet**! **Kook**, you start on your **ash tray**!

Some prison! This is ridiculous!

If you think **this** is bad, just wait until "Color War"!

What did **he** do?

He went **swimming** without his **buddy**!

Where are they **taking** him?

They're putting him in **the box**!

What **happens** in the box?

He has to watch "Hud", "Harper", "Hombre" and "The Hustler" without a break!

That stuff don't bother **me**! I'm **detatched**! I'm **cut off** from Society! I don't need **anything** . . . or **anybody**!

Oh, yeah!? What kind of a guy **ARE** you, anyway!?

So lonely, I could **DIE**!!

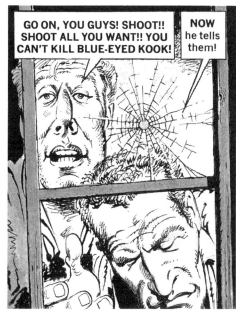

BALMY

Some people have asked me how I happen to be **qualified** to **produce** films at my age. Well, actually I am a **great student** of the motion picture. In fact, I've seen **every** movie that **Walt Disney** ever made. I just **love** his adorable little animals. And now, **speaking** of adorable little animals, here is the story of . . .

AND CLOD

ARTIST: MORT DRUCKER   WRITER: LARRY SIEGEL

Hoo—boy, are you stupid!

Well, Ah **tol'** you Ah'm a part-time moron! An' Ah'm **"On Duty"** now!

Call us **"Robin Hoods"**! We robs from the **poor** an' we gives to **ourselves** Haw, haw, haw!

Ain't they the **cutest couple**, Paw?

They so adorable, Ah could take big **bites** out of them.

Mark mah words, they **goin' places**. They such lovable, hilarious crooks, you jus' **gotta** love 'em.

Ah been robbed by **many great comics** in the past . . **Dillinger, Baby-Face Nelson** . . . but **these two**— they the **funniest!**

Oh, Clod, waren't that **fun?** We gonna have such a happy life together. **Kiss me! Hug me! Make out** with me!

No makin' out! Ah **cain't** make out with you!

You cain't make out with me? **Why?** 'Cause you got problems? 'Cause you **sick?** 'Cause you need a **haid doctor?**

No, 'cause Ah happen t' be drivin' this car at eighty miles an hour!

The following article is rated "G"...which means it's Okay for General Audiences. However, t
following article is a MAD satire of an "X"-rated movie...which means the movie is dirty, a
Children Under 16 are Not Permitted to see it. Which further means that if you are under 16, y
couldn't possibly have seen the movie, and therefore you cannot possibly enjoy this MAD sat

MIDNIGHT

ARTIST: MORT DRUCK

f it. So use your dopey, under-16 head for a change! Don't laugh at this article if your parents
re around, or you'll give it away that you lied about your age and sneaked in to see the movie!
Incidentally, if your parents laugh at this article, it means they must have seen the movie, and
ou can ask them what in heck they were doing, going to see a dirty movie anyhow!) Here, then, is…

WOWBOY

WRITER: STAN HART

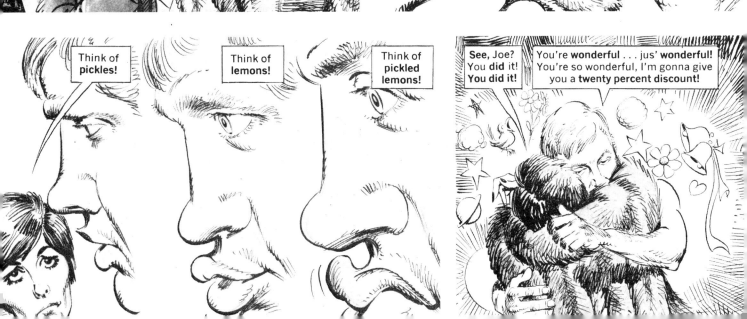

In times past, Hollywood has turned out some big, corny movie musicals. But the biggest, corniest movie musical of all is now playing. Sure, the songs are lovely, but take them away and what have you got? Nothing but a collection of the same old dull clichés and boring tear-jerker gimmicks that you've been seeing in movie musicals for years. (We're even falling asleep writing this introduction about it!) It's obvious that this motion picture was made with only one goal in mind: Mainly to hear

THE $SOUND OF MONEY

How come I'm alone, and there's so much music?
gh up on a hill, with no one in view?
how do they get all this sound and music?
nusical quiz I now pose to you.

Just see how I race up this steep mountainside
Without ever losing a beat!
You'd think that my lungs would give out up here
Over ten thousand feet!

To do all these things
with a wide-mouthed grin
Really should not amaze;
I've had lots of rest,
'Cause they filmed it on five different days!

I'm not singing now; I am pre-recorded!
I'm just mouthing words I have sung before!
And how does it feel to be singing nothing?
It's an aw-ful bore!

ARTIST: MORT DRUCKER
WRITER: STAN HART

"Sung to the tune of "The Sound of Music"

*Sung to the tune of "How Do You Solve A Problem Like Maria?"

Just show a kookie Nun who rides a scooter;
Or show a Sister try to fly a kite.
The movies can make folks feel
That all these events are real,
And being a Nun is fun from morn' till night!
People will eat up films about religion!
Just keep them cor-ny, sacch-ar-in and trite!

Ingrid Bergman, you'll recall,
As a Nun would play baseball;
And sweet Audrey Hepburn,
    Convent life forswore;
Sister Debbie was so swinging
On her motorbike, while singing;
Old Roz Russell, Donna Reed, and many more.

All the Nuns sang a lament
While they mixed up their cement,
Playing "Lilies Of The Field" with so much zeal;
Deborah Kerr was quite specific
On that spot in the Pacific;
Celeste Holm, Loretta Young all had appeal.
Yes . . . everyone loves a picture on religion—
Long as the Nuns and Priests are so unreal!

I'm **tired** of hanging around the country! I'm going to **Vienna** and hang around the **city** for a while!

While your father's away, let's have a little **fun!** We'll go **bicycle riding, hiking, swimming** and **picnicking!**

That's okay with **us**, but what's it got to do with this **story?**

Nothing at all! But movie fans **love** to see scenes where unhappy kids are finally having a good time! It's **commercial!** And **remember!** We're not in this movie for our **health!** We're in it for **the MONEY!!**

*****DOUGH . . .** Means cash for all of us! **RAY . . .** For musicals like this!

*Sung to the tune of "Do...Re...Mi"

ME . . . A "Star" so big that by **FAR . . .** It couldn't really miss!

SO . . . Insipid is the plot; **LA—** Dee-Da, although we know, **TEE—** Dee-ous it is, a lot,

It will bring us Back much **DOUGH . . . DOUGH . . . DOUGH . . . DOUGH . . .**

Captain, I've heard your children **sing**, and I think they have a **great future** working in **Show Business!**

They can **never** do that! It would violate a **Von Tripe tradition** dating back **six centuries!**

What tradition?

Continuous Unemployment!

Mitzia, I think the Captain is in **love** with you!

B-but, Countess! I love the **Captain!** If it's **true** that **he** loves me, then I must **leave!** And if **that** doesn't make any **sense** to **you**, it makes even **less** to me! But **I** didn't write this picture! Did **anyone?**

Mother Obsess, I want to come back to the Convent!

You can't come **here** to escape the **outside world**, Mitzia!

Why not??

Because **we** came **here** to escape from **you!!**

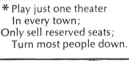

*Sung to the tune of "Climb Every Mountain!"

DE SADEST STORY EVER TOLD DEPT.

Us moral people all hate violence, right? Let's hear it for "Anti-Violence"! *Yayyy!* Stanley Kubrick also hates violence, right? Let's hear it for Stanley Kubrick! *Yayyy!* And let's hear it for his new movie, which shows how horrible violence is! *Yay*— Uh— Hey, wait a minute! If Mr. Kubrick's new movie is so "Anti-Violence," how come it's jam-packed with the worst, sickening, most disgusting violence imaginable? Let's face it, Stanley, baby! Your movie is really . . .

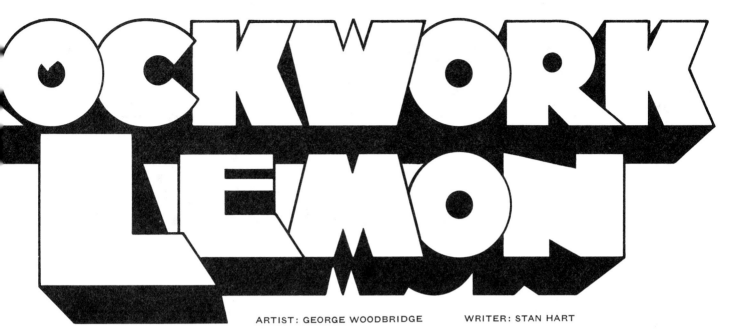

OCKWORK LEMON

ARTIST: GEORGE WOODBRIDGE   WRITER: STAN HART

Why are you doing this to me? All I ask for is a little **kindness!**

To **US,** this **IS** kindness!

And you'd better say, **"Thank you!"**, 'cause Alecch **hates** an ingrate!

So long, Pops! Stay out of trouble!

In **traction,** you can get into **trouble?!?**

That was **great!** What's **next,** Alecch?

How about a nice little gang **war?**

Swell!! I'll sock **you**—then you belt Gouger—

With **ANOTHER gang,** Dimwit, you dimwit!

Blimey! When you blokes said you'd get me on the **STAGE,** I didn't think you meant **THIS!!**

Hey, Bilgey Boy, How about a **knife fight?**

Okay, Alecch

Gee . . . does this mean our **date's off?**

Sorry, but I got **business** to attend to!

At **two pounds apiece,** what do you think **I** was doing?!

So . . .? How've you been?

Not bad! Read any good **books** lately?

Looks like we're in for some **rain!**

My Uncle Irving changed **dentists!**

INSIDE DOPE DEPT.

There's a great movie playing around. It's exciting, and full of action, and it's easy to watch. It's not one of those movies where you have to think! Or is it?? You certainly don't do any thinking during the movie. But after it's over, you're left with a couple of unanswered questions. In fact, *everybody* is left with a couple of unanswered questions. Take f'rinstance the guy who gets shot in the very first scenes:

BLAM BLAM

Okay! So I walked around Marseilles! So this brown Mark III Lincoln Continental followed me! So I bought a French bread, and I bought a pizza, and I stepped into this doorway, and now I'm being—GAAAK! —murdered! So after the picture is all over, maybe somebody will tell me . . .

WHAT'S THE CONNECTION?

ARTIST: MORT DRUCKER   WRITER: DICK DE BARTOLO

Hey, Birdie! Did you **see**? That guy gave the waiter a **$100 tip!**

It's not even **his waiter!** And now he's giving the hat check girl a **$50 tip!**

He doesn't even have a **hat!** There's something **fishy** going on here! That kind of tipping makes me **suspicious!** And the fact that they're all wearing **GUNS** doesn't **help!** C'mon! Let's follow 'em!

Cockeye, the **last** time we followed someone, we **stayed up** for **3 days and 3 nights**, went **48 hours without food**, and **accidentally killed a Federal Agent!**

Well . . . I can't promise it will be as much fun as **THAT**— but let's give it a whirl!

Well? What's so unusual about **that?**

Well? What's so unusual about **that?**

Gee, Cockeye, you're doing a **great job** of staying right on their **tail!**

No problem, Birdie! I tied our **bumpers** together!

But don't you think they'll get a **little suspicious**— seeing the **same car** behind them five hours in a row—especially in **deserted Brooklyn?!?**

Naw! I keep changing my expression and they think I'm **someone different** each time they look!

Hey! The guy drives a **Caddy**, his girl is loaded down with **expensive clothes and jewelry**, and they come home to a **dumpy little Candy Store** like **that!** What do you **think**, Cockeye?

I think that Candy Store is a **GOLD MINE!** We should open one **right across the street** and steal his **customers!**

I'm going to **New York!**

I bought you a new **camera!**

I bought you a **new coat!**

That's **great!** Now **tell** me, what's the **connection?**

I got the scoop on those **Candy Store sweeties!** His name is **Salvatore Giuseppe Bocciballo**, and his wife's name is **Angelina Bocciballo!**

Oh, they're **Italians?**

No, **Wops!**

Wasn't this a **great idea** of mine? I figured Bocciballo was getting a little suspicious of seeing a **car** behind him all the time, so I came up with **this . . .**

Yeah, but don't you think that **sitting in** his **BACK SEAT** is a little **dangerous?**

Not so **loud!** He'll **hear** you! Now this is what I found out so far! Bocciballo and his wife make about **$7000 a year** from the Candy Store . . . and they spend **$80,000!**

Boy, I wish **MY** wife could **stretch a buck** like **that!**

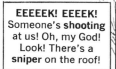

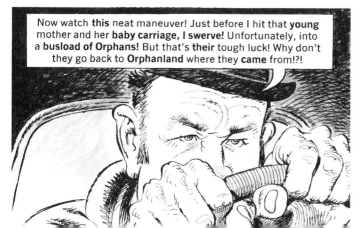

d YOU—you @#¢$%&! cheap ttle eight-year old @#$%¢&! Better stop **peeking** at this #$%¢&! story at the **magazine** rack and **BUY** your own copy, or I'll draft your @#$%¢&! ght into the @#$%¢&! **Army!**

Now, here's my military philosophy! No @#$%¢&! ever won a war by dying for his country! You win a war by letting the **OTHER** @#$%¢&! die for **HIS** country!

And **HOW** do you let the **OTHER** @#$%¢&! die for his country? You **KILL** the other @#$%¢&! **THAT'S how!**

So if you want to win a war, you gotta **kill every other** @#$%¢&! And if that includes **ENEMY** @#$%¢&!'s— so much the **better!** All right! You will now sit and pay attention and you will begin reading this story about killing other @#$%¢&!'s . . . and you will **finish** it . . . and you will **enjoy** it . . . and that's a @#$%¢&! **order!** Otherwise, you'll answer to . . .

PUT ★ ON

ARTIST: MORT DRUCKER   WRITER: LARRY SIEGEL

America's **first taste of battle,** Gen Boredly, and the Nazis gave us a **terrible beating!** Look at those **Arabs** stripping our dead soldiers of their **clothing . . . !**

Death is **everywhere,** Harris! God, how I **hate** the stench of death!

That's not **death** you smell, Sir! That's those **Arabs . . .** and their **camels!**

God, how I **miss** the stench of death!

What's **wrong** with our troops, Harris? They don't seem to respond to my **leadership!** Tell me why!

The men just don't **respect** you, Sir! No offense meant, Sir—but they consider you a **crashing bore!**

A crashing **bore?!**

Yes, Sir! You know how Hitler is called **"Der Fuehrer"** and Rommel is called **"The Desert Fox"**?

Right! What's my nickname?

"The Insurance Salesman"!

That's a **LIE!** I'm **NOT** a bore! I'm a dynamic, vibrant officer!

YOU!! Stop trying to steal my **clothes!** Leave me alone! I'm not dead!

You're **NOT?!** Boy, you sure had **ME** fooled!

Hmmmm! Okay, I get the **message!** We need a **more dynamic leader** here . . . a **fearless** and **colorful** personality to **uplift** and **inspire** the troops! And I know **just the man!**

Hey, Willie . . . you ever hear of **General George Put★on?**

Nah, Joe! Who's he?

He's gonna be our new **leader!**

Ahh, when you've seen **ONE** Commanding General, you've see 'em all!

You!! **Soldier!** Look **alive** when I talk to you! You call yourself a member of the **U.S. Army?** I say you're a @ # $ % ¢ & ! **disgrace!** Look at your @ # $ % ¢ & ! **uniform!** Look at your @ # $ % ¢ & ! **posture!** You're confined to your @ # ¢ $ % & ! barracks for the **rest of this war** . . . and for the first two years of the **next** war . . . if we **have** another one—**God willing!!**

Well . . . don't just **stand there!** DISMISSED!!

Wow! If that's how he talks to his **superior officers, WE'RE DEAD!!!**

This is the **filthiest** @ # $ % ¢ & ! barrack I've **ever seen!** Dirty **floors** . . . dirty **walls** . . . dirty **beds!** And what's **this?!** DIRTY PIN-UP PICTURES?!?

Is that all you can think about, Soldier? **Dirty** @ # ¢ $ % & ! **SEX!**

Not exactly, Sir—

You want **exciting fantasies at night?** I'll give you **MY** pin-up pictures to hang! 8 x 10 glossies of **mutilated Germans!**

But, Sir! I don't think you know—

What would your **Mother** say if she saw this picture? Your gray-haired, kind, loveable **American Mother** . . . sitting at home, knitting for the Red Cross and baking apple pie! Soldier, you've got a **dirty mind!**

B-but, Sir! That pin-up picture **IS** my Mother!!

Soldier . . . you've got a dirty Mother!!

Next barracks! **Hmmm!** What are **these** men doing in **bed?** It's past 0500! Everyone on your feet for **close order drill**— then five laps around Morocco!

Okay! Make it **FOUR** laps around Morocco! And men with leg wounds can **crawl!**

But, Sir! This is a **hospital!**

Now, what's **YOUR** problem, Soldier?

I've got **shrapnel** in my back, General!

Well, don't just **lie there!** As long as you're in that **position,** DO PUSH-UPS!!

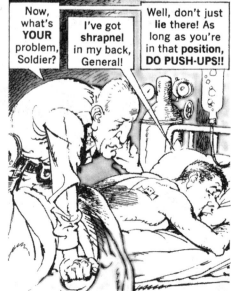

What's wrong with him?

He's **dead,** Sir!

That's **no** excuse! Make him **stand at attention!**

Look at all these wonderfully wounded GI's from my #%¢&! Messina campaign! Look at all these beautiful wounds!

Love that wound, Soldier! It's so clean, so deep, so American! Keep it always! Don't ever let it heal!

It'll be OUR wound, okay?

Yes, sir!

Why is he kissing that Soldier?

Because he needs an emotional release! Because he needs to make a soldierly gesture of battle-field cameraderie!

But . . . why is he bending that soldier's head back until it's touching the floor? And . . . why is he kissing him on the mouth?

Because he also needs a BROAD so bad!!

What's the matter with YOU?

Tired?! How come you're not wounded?! Why aren't you bleeding like the rest of these men? What's the matter, you too good to bleed? If there's anything I can't stand, it's a NON-BLEEDER!!

I'm just t-tired, Sir . . .

I'm s-sorry, Sir! I j-just can't fight!

Can't fight?! You COWARD!! Give this @#¢$%&! coward a gun, and send him into combat!!

Stop him! He'll tear that man's head off! Quick— get the Chief Surgeon!

I've got news for you . . . That IS the Chief Surgeon!

That explains it! No WONDER he said he can't fight! Better call the Chaplain!

I can't! He's in bed with a broken jaw! Don't you remember? HE told the General he couldn't fight, TOO!

Now hear this! I recently slapped a Chief Surgeon . . . and punched a Chaplain! Gen. Eisenhower told me I shouldn't have done it! So this is what I want to say about that:

@#$%¢&! @#¢$%&! @#¢$%&!

Gee, I've never seen him swallow his pride like this before!

It takes a really BIG man to say he's sorry and apologize!

So much for Sicily! Now, on to Europe! God, how I love war! I love the killing, the maiming, the wounding, the destruction! And I even love the UGLY parts of war, too!

Why aren't you men killing?!

Sir, we've been in combat 24-hours-day for three weeks now! We're exhausted! We were just taking a quick ten-minute break . . .

Fine! You're entitled to one! But don't just SIT there! STEP ON ANTS!!

Hi, War Movie fans! I'm **John Wayne!** I just want to say, after making such **distinguished War Pictures** as *"Sands Of Iwo Jima," "Flying Leathernecks," "Back To Bataan"* and *"The Fighting Seabees,"* that I found this **recent** War Movie an **affront** to **good taste!**

Hi! I'm **Dana Andrews!** I just want to say, after making such **distinguished War Pictures** as *"Purple Heart," "The Best Years of Our Lives"* and *"A Walk In The Sun,"* that I found this **recent** War Movie an **affront** to **good taste!**

Hi! I'm **Adolph Hitler!** I just want to say, after making such **distinguished Wars** as *"The Rape of Poland," "The Fall of France," "The Siege of Britain," "The Invasion of Russia"* and *"The Genocide of Millions,"* that even I found this recent War Movie an **affront** to **good taste!** So it **MUST** be ecchy!!

With these comments in mind, MAD Magazine now brings you an even worse affront to good taste! Mainly, our version of . . .

M*I*S*H M*O*S*H

ARTIST: ANGELO TORRES   WRITER: ARNIE KOGEN

Hi, buddy! My name is **Squawkeye!** I'm a **new replacement Surgeon!**

Hi! My name is **Kook! I'm** a new replacement Surgeon, **too!**

Great! Hop in! We'll **start off** the picture by **stealing a Jeep,** thereby showing **complete irreverence for authority** . . . and **also** pulling the **first** of many outrageous pranks!

What's so **outrageous** about **stealing a Jeep?**

This one belongs to **President Truman!**

There they go . . . trying to cash in on the **"Youth Market"** with another anti-Establishment, low-budget picture!

What's so **low budget** about the **Korean War?**

Well, when you compare it to the War in Vietnam . . .

WELCOME TO KOREA CAL.

USA I THINK...

HST 471 MISSOURI 51

DON'T MISH MOSH TURN PAGE →

Hey, Gang! Tired of all the garbage they're showing on motion picture screens lately? Well, here's a "Family" film for a change! And now, meet the "Family":

This is Don Vino Minestrone. Not too long ago, he was just a poor immigrant from Sicily. Now he's a leading racketeer, extortionist and killer. How did Don Vino get where he is today? By putting his faith in The American Way of Life.

Here's Mama Minestrone, a typical lovable Sicilian housewife. It seems like only yesterday at another wedding that Mama herself said, "I do!" Come to think of it, that was the last time she opened her mouth.

This is Don Vino's daughter, Canny, and her bridegroom, Carly. Such a nice couple. Everyone is saying that Don Vino is not really losing a daughter. No, actually, in this kind of Family, he'll probably lose a Son-in-law.

And so, with such a strange family and such weird children,

THE ODD

This is Sinny Minestrone, the Don's eldest son. He's next in line, and it's only a matter of time before he gets the Family business. That is, of course, unless a rival Family decides to give him the business first.

This is the Don's second son, Freako. He's a sad, gentle soul. He cries at weddings and all kinds of Family crises. But he can also be a barrel of laughs. Just catch him at a funeral some time.

This is Tim Haven, the Don's adopted son. He's shrewd and smart. All his life, he dreamed of being a criminal lawyer. But he only finished half of his education —the "criminal" part.

And this is Micrin, the Don's youngest son. He's a college graduate, a veteran war hero, an honest law-abiding citizen —and a disgrace to the entire Family.

t's easy to see why Don Vino Minestrone is known as...

FATHER

ARTIST: MORT DRUCKER

WRITER: LARRY SIEGEL

What a fantastic **make-up** job they've done on **Marlin Brandow!** How did they ever get him to look so **OLD?**

Very simple! They made him watch his **last four movies,** and he aged **20 years!**

I still can't believe it's Marlin Brandow!

Mumble mumble mumble mumble

It's **Marlin Brandow,** all right!!

...IT IS YOUR HONOR TO INVITE ME TO YOUR DAUGHTER'S BRISS...

Papa, I'm so **happy** on my Wedding Day! Why aren't **you** happy **too?** Why do you look so **pained?!?**

You think it's **easy** to see your little girl **grow up?** You think it's **easy** to give her away to **another man?** You think it's **easy** to talk with **eight pounds of cotton** in your cheeks?

But **you** talk like that **WITHOUT** cotton in your cheeks!

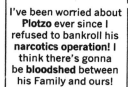

I've been worried about **Plotzo** ever since I refused to bankroll his **narcotics operation!** I think there's gonna be **bloodshed** between his Family and ours!

Maybe you shouldn't be walking the **streets** like this, Papa!

What could possibly **happen** to me here on **Mulberry Street** in **New York?** Could I be harmed by that cute Italian **fish peddler?** By those sweet Italian **kids,** playing Hop-Scotch? By those nice Italian **button men** in their big black car . . . barreling down on me at 80 miles an hour? **OH-OH!!**

He—he's **DEAD!** Did the hoods in that **big black car** gun him down?

Not exactly! I think they **WANTED** to! But when they got within **50 feet** of him, a **mugger** who was stealing a woman's **purse** ran into the path of a **highjacked truck** going the **wrong way** on a **"One-Way"** street which swerved into a **drug pusher's stolen motorcycle,** and they **all fell on top of** him! In other words, he died of **natural causes!**

Natural causes?!

In **New York,** that's natural causes!

Hey, **wait a minute!** He's **NOT dead after all!** He's trying to **speak!**

What's he **saying?**

It's hard to **tell!** He's **hurt** so bad, he's talking through his **nose!**

I got **news** for you! He talks like that when he's **NOT** hurt, **too!**

What **is** it, Micrin?

I just got **bad news!** My Father is **badly hurt!** He's been lying in the street for **three days!**

Why don't they put him in the **hospital?**

He won't tell them his **Blue Cross number!**

I've heard of the **Mafia** keeping secrets, but that's ridiculous!

Thank God we finally got him into the hospital! How is he, Doctor?

Well, he's **retching!** And he's **coughing!** And he's **gasping for breath!** And he's **moaning a lot!**

He's fighting for his **life?!?**

No, he's fighting for an **"Oscar"!**

MAD'S "LATE SHOW"
CLICHÉ MOVIE SCRIPT

ARTIST: BRUCE STARK   WRITER: HARRY PURVIS

THE "OPERA" MOVIE

"You have a charming little voice, my dear. However, it needs training--a great deal of training! You understand that if I, Vittorio Calamare, take you on as my protegee, it will mean years of hard work. There will be no time for the unimportant things that most girls dream about--things like love and marriage."

*   *   *   *   *   *

"Don't you see, Mike? It's my big chance. You can't ask me to give it up. Not now! Not after I've worked so hard!"

*   *   *   *   *   *

"Signore e Signori, it is with regret that I must make the following announcement. Due to illness, Mme. Lucia Maledizione will not sing tonight. However, in her place, I am pleased to present--in her debut performance--Miss Irene Fairly..."

*   *   *   *   *   *

"Go ahead, my dear, and do not be nervous. They will love you!"

*   *   *   *   *   *

"Poor kid, they're not giving her a chance. This crowd came to hear the great Maledizione, and no one else. Wait--isn't that Vittorio Calamare himself, walking out onto the stage?"

*   *   *   *   *   *

"You call yourselves opera lovers? Then ACT like it! This girl is my pupil! Would I consent to this appearance if I did not believe she could sing the role of 'Zuccini' as it has never been sung before?!"

*   *   *   *   *   *

"Listen to that applause! Even Maledizione at her best never received such an ovation! We are watching opera history being made tonight!"

*   *   *   *   *   *

"Yes, I was there tonight! Mike, the cow hand, in his forty dollar suit, standing among the white ties and tails. But even I saw it, Irene--even I know now that you've been given a great gift...a gift that belongs to the world! I have no right to ask you to waste it on some little cattle ranch in the middle of nowhere!"

*   *   *   *   *   *

"...and after London, Irene--we go to Milan! Think of it! No American coloratura has ever sing the role of 'Fettucine' at 'La Scala' before!"

*   *   *   *   *   *

"But, Vittorio! You promised that when this tour was over I could have a vacation! I want to go home, Vittorio! I'm...tired...<u>sob</u>..."

*   *   *   *   *   *

"Ladies and gentlemen, thank you. You are much too kind. To sing at 'The Met' is privilege enough...but my statue at the entrance--well, what can I say?! It makes it even harder for me to tell you...that...that this was my LAST PERFORMANCE! No--no, please--you mustn't! You see, after tonight, Irene Fairly will be no more! She will become, instead, just plain Mrs. Mike Nolan of Butte, Montana! That is--if he'll still have me! I hope you're listening, Mike...because this is my farewell aria--and I dedicate it to you..."

*   *   *   *   *   *

"Maestro...would you please play "Home On The Range" in the key of High C...?"

THE END

When they first set out to make a film of this successful Broadway play, they decided that they'd need two middle-aged ugly people to play the hero and heroine. Then they decided that they'd also like to make *money* with this film!

So they hired Liz and Dick! You won't *believe* how the make-up man has camouflaged Liz's beauty and sex appeal—turning her into an ugly, middle-aged bag! Brace yourself! Here comes that hideous, overblown, sexless blob now!

See those three lines around her eyes! And see those four grey hairs! And see how ugly she looks all over! Yeccchhh! All we know is: We certainly wouldn't want our mother to look like her! Our *girl friend,* yeah! But not our mother!

Now get ready for a movie excursion into the world of sex, profanity, screaming, drinking and blood-curdling parlor games that never quite answers the question the whole world is asking . . . mainly:

WHO IN HECK IS VIRGINIA WOOLFE?

ARTIST: MORT DRUCKER   WRITER: LARRY SIEGEL

Well, here we are . . . me, the dirty rotten daughter of a University President . . . and you, a dirty rotten History Teacher! It's two o'clock in the morning and we've just returned from a Faculty Party to our dirty rotten home!

Right! And now, we're going to play dirty rotten **games** for the rest of the night! Because, through these games, the author plans to dramatically strip away our facades and reveal the fulsome phantasmagoria of base rot that permeates our souls!

That sounds **deep!** What in blazes does it **mean?**

It means that this is an **Art Film**—so now the Censors will **have** to let us talk dirty!

THE WRONG ARM OF THE LAW DEPT.

Say! What ever happened to those "nice" movie detectives of years ago? Remember? They were all pleasant, good-natured guys with no hang-ups. *Charlie Chan*, the *Thin Man* . . . even the *Shadow* enjoyed a healthy laugh once in a while. But look what's happening today. Every new movie detective that comes along appears to have a problem. You know who we're talking about. Detectives like moody, semi-bewildered Steve McQueen in "Bullet" . . . bigoted, neurotic Gene Hackman in "The French Connection" . . . and now **this** guy: a taciturn, trigger-happy, morose, sadistic, psychotic farblungit known as—what else?—

DIRT

Y LARRY

ARTIST:
MORT DRUCKER

WRITER:
ARNIE KOGEN

Him?! He's a film Detective?! He can't be! He's too good-looking! He's not blind or in a wheelchair! He has no . . . no HANDICAPS!

He hasn't; eh? Well— just wait! He's about to reveal his handicap: his lovable personality!

Hello! I'm Dirty Larry Killerman! I'm tough, hard-nosed, bitter and sardonic! And I DON'T like to be kept waiting, Mayor LaGuardia!

LaGuardia?!? He was Mayor of New York during the 1930's and the 1940's!

I told you what I am! I never said I was bright!

Killerman, the City of San Francisco is being terrorized by a mad killer! You've been on the case for ten minutes! What've you done about it?

I searched the Ponderosa, bashed in the OK Corral and splattered the blood of ten Mexican banditos all over Juarez!

Poor Clint! He's done so many "Spaghetti Westerns," he's got his movies confused!

Quick! While I slowly chew my sandwich, call this number and tell them there's a 311 in progress!

A 311? Is that a robbery in the bank??

No, that's botulism in your food!

Botulism?!? How can you tell?

I'm a cop, that's how! Before I sat down, I "stopped and frisked" the meatloaf!

Now comes the big scene where I calmly shoot four bank robbers while continuing to eat my lunch! Actually, the sight of all that blood gives me an appetite!

It's amazing! All this gun-play and you're still chewing so slowly!!

To tell you the truth, it's impossible to chew fast when you're eating a "Bullet Sandwich"!

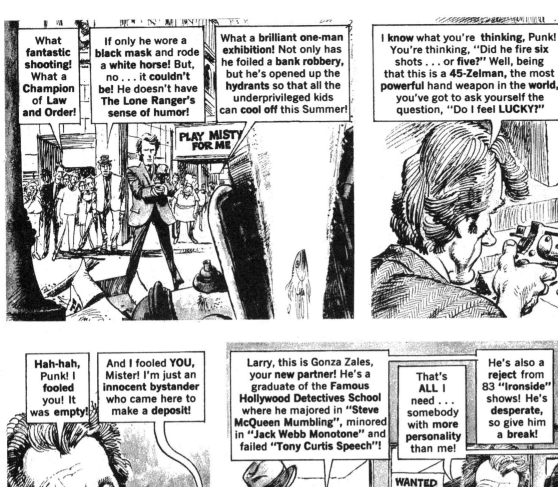

What fantastic shooting! What a Champion of Law and Order!

If only he wore a black mask and rode a white horse! But, no . . . it couldn't be! He doesn't have The Lone Ranger's sense of humor!

What a brilliant one-man exhibition! Not only has he foiled a bank robbery, but he's opened up the hydrants so that all the underprivileged kids can cool off this Summer!

I know what you're thinking, Punk! You're thinking, "Did he fire six shots . . . or five?" Well, being that this is a 45-Zelman, the most powerful hand weapon in the world, you've got to ask yourself the question, "Do I feel LUCKY?"

Mister, I'm just a deprived kid from the ghetto who's currently bleeding to death! Must you add "boring riddles" to all my other problems?! Let me die in dignity . . . without the cliches, huh?!?

Hah-hah, Punk! I fooled you! It was empty!

And I fooled YOU, Mister! I'm just an innocent bystander who came here to make a deposit!

Larry, this is Gonza Zales, your new partner! He's a graduate of the Famous Hollywood Detectives School where he majored in "Steve McQueen Mumbling", minored in "Jack Webb Monotone" and failed "Tony Curtis Speech"!

That's ALL I need . . . somebody with more personality than me!

He's also a reject from 83 "Ironside" shows! He's desperate, so give him a break!

But I'm a Loner, I tell you! I don't need a partner! And especially him! He's a creep and a meathead and a screw-up!

C'mon, Dirty Larry! Don't beat around the bush! Do you want me as your partner or don't you?

Look! There's our killer now! He's about to shoot a Negro Homosexual in the park!

Quick! Let's grab him! We gotta rid the streets of his kind of slime and filth!

Wait! You're going the wrong way! The killer's in THAT direction!

What killer?!? I'M talking about the Homosexual!

Why do they call you "Dirty"? Because you hate everybody?

Because you're to the right of Archie Bunker . . . politically?

Because you've got a pin-up of Adolf Hitler in your locker?

. . . Because you like to peep in on innocent people making love, thereby violating their Constitutional freedoms?

No!

No!

No!

Say, you DID go to Detective School . . . DIDN'T you?!?

Well, we've got that maniac trapped!

Yeah, we've got him **so** trapped, he's gonna kill us any second!

I tell you, he's in **big trouble** . . . shooting at a **Super Star**! He's gonna get **his** before this movie is over!

Super Star? You mean **YOU?!?**

No, I mean the guy on the sign!

Boy, you zanies really got ol' Libra **sore** this time! Now he's holding a **17-year-old girl hostage**, and he's **raised the ante**! He wants **$200,000** . . . plus **$100 a day** expenses, plus **$4.00 a bullet**, plus **carfare**!

Hey, who **IS** this psycho? He's insane!

I don't know, but **whoever** he is, I'd like him to **represent me** on my next 3 movie deals!

Okay, if **I'm** gonna be the **bag man** for this caper, I'm gonna be ready for **trouble**!

Hey, it's the old **"Taping The Knife To The Ankle"** trick, eh? Good thinking, Larry! Libra will **never** get out of this alive!

That ankle knife is **NOT** for Libra!

No? Then what . . . ?

It's another of Dirty Larry's peculiar prejudices! He loves to kick midgets!

This is **Libra**! Do you have the yellow bag with the **$205,000** in it?

$205,000?!? But you said **$200,000**!

That was during **Phase I**! Nixon's economic plans are screwing us all up! *Tee-hee! Giggle . . . giggle . . . giggle!*

Now, **listen**, Pig! To make sure you're **not followed**, I'm gonna run you around a little . . .

. . . so here are your instructions, Pig! You're gonna run from **phone booth** to **phone booth** till you're **exhausted**! You're gonna start in **Fillmore**, run through the **tunnel** to a **Chicken Delight stand**, then pick up a **cable car**, get off, run across the **Bay Bridge** and meet me under the cross in **Prospect Park**!

Prospect Park?!? But . . . that's in **BROOKLYN**!

I **TOLD** you I was gonna run you around a little!

YOU'LL KNOW ME . . . I'M WEARING A WHITE CARNATION!

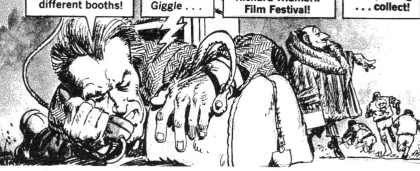
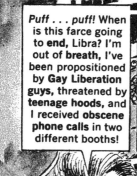

Puff . . . puff! When is this farce going to **end**, Libra? I'm out of **breath**, I've been propositioned by **Gay Liberation** guys, threatened by **teenage hoods**, and I received **obscene phone calls** in two different booths!

Boy, it's **not safe** on the streets for **decent people** like me anymore! *Tee-hee-hee! Giggle . . . Giggle . . . Giggle . . .*

This is **amazing!** As **bad** as I've been **UNDERacting**, you're **OVERacting!** Where'd you learn that "B" movie laugh?

When I was a kid, I was frightened by a **Richard Widmark Film Festival!**

Well, I **gotta hang up** now! I wanna do **one** more "**mean**" thing before we meet! I'm gonna call an **Orphanage** . . . collect!

Now comes the scene where I **pummel you senseless**, kick you in the ribs and stomp on your **neck** . . . while you **stab** me viciously in the **leg**, and I, in turn, spot your **partner** tailing me in the **bushes** and shoot portions of his **body** away from **other** portions of his **body** in **one wild bloody mess!**

What **ski mask?** It's an **Eskimo Airlines "sickness bag"!** Even I can't stomach all this violence!

Okay! But tell me, why the **ski mask?**

RAT-TAT-TAT

Punk, is there some **perverse reason** why you chose this site for your **blood-shed?** Does it mean you're **anti-God?**

Oh, no! In my own way, I'm **very religious!** I worship **Kayu**, the Norse God of "**Senseless Brutality**"!

Then why not **give yourself up?** With professional help and rehabilitation, you can be trained to worship **Seymour**, the Norse God of "**Malicious Mischief**"!

That creep won't get away from me **again!** This time, I've tracked him down to his home here in **Kezar Stadium!** But it can't be! A psycho killer like that—a **Sports Fan?!?** It doesn't make any **sense** . . .

Oh-oh! **This** explains it! He eats the "**Breakfast of Runners-Up**"!

I got you at last, punk! Tell me where the **girl** is, or I'll beat it out of you!

Please! **Not here!**

What do you mean, not here?

Not on **Astroturf!** I suffer much better on genuine grass!

You really get a **charge** out of torturing me, **don't** you, Pig . . . ?

Are you kidding? I can't wait to see this on "**Instant Replay**"!

I have rights! Haven't you heard of the **4th Amendment?**

No, but if it's anywhere near the **3rd Vertebra**, I think I just kicked it in!

Mr. District Attorney . . . what do you mean, you're letting that killer go free?!?

That "alleged" killer!

But yesterday, they buried the victim's "alleged" body!

We have **no case!** You violated the suspect's **rights** when you broke into his **home** without a search warrant! Isn't that **right,** Judge Slapwrist?

In all my **legal** experience, Killerman, I've **never** seen anything **like** it! You clumsily violated the **Constitution** and the **entire** Bill of Rights!

Okay! So I made a few technical mistakes! Does that mean you're gonna let a **killer** roam the streets?

We are **forced to,** Mr. Killerman! Remember— it's **Laws** like that which make America **great!**

Well, me and the **audience** just decided we like the **Laws** that made **Nazi Germany** great!

Do you have anything **further** to say, Lieut. Killerman?

Yes! Before I kick the two of you in the **groin,** I would like to warn you of your **rights!**

I know you've been **trailing** me, Pig! I know you've been **following** me around town! You came in here to **stare** at me, didn't you?

Take a **good** look around, Creep! Boy, not only are you **violent** . . . you're **also stupid!**

TOTALLY NUDE COLLEGE COEDS

GIRLS GIRLS

NO COVER NO MIN

Here's $200! **Beat** me up!

Man, that's **freaky!** Why would anyone want to do that?

It's not my idea! It's the **Producers'!** They figure the movie hasn't had any **violence** for the **past seven seconds!**

Why spend $200? I have some "**Bargain Specials**"!

Bargain Specials? F'rinstance?

Well, for **$169.50,** I slap you silly with **open fists!** For **$99,** I twist your **nose** like "**The 3 Stooges!**" And for only **$24.95,** I have an **Interior Decorator** come and "**tweak**" you to death!

Naw, I like this! Just throw in a **karate chop to the gut** and I'll leave you a nice **tip!**

What **publicity** he's maneuvered for himself! He's on TV . . . claiming that **you beat him up!**

Anyone can get on "**The 6 O'Clock News**"!

What "**News**"? He's this week's **Guest Host** on the "**Johnny Carson Show**"!

So Gonza Zales is quitting the force! Well, I'm gonna **miss** him! He was a **good** partner! His poker face . . . his total lack of expression . . . his **monotone!**

If **that's** what he was like, why are you going to **miss** him!?

Because he was the "**lively one**" of the team!

That **Libra** has **struck again!** He's kidnapped a **school bus** full of kids! And **this** time he wants **$300,000!!**

What's the **extra** $100,000 for?

For **stationery** to write **more ransom** notes! He claim's he's **running short!**

The Cops Close In

ART—MORT DRUCKER

KING CON DEPT.

Throughout the years, Hollywood has given us many beautiful couples...Ginger Rogers and Fred Astaire, Elizabeth Taylor and Richard Burton, Ryan O'Neal and Ali McGraw... but, unquestionably, the most *beautiful* movie couple of *all* is Paul Newman and Robert Redford. "Beautiful" not only in the physical sense, but for Theater Owners in terms of Box Office Receipts. And, as is always the case, in order to capitalize on a movie success, Hollywood has come up with a "sequel"! Yep, if you like charm, wit, style and nostalgia...well, then, go see "Butch Cassidy And The Sundance Kid." *That* movie had *all* those elements. As far as *this sequel* is concerned, we don't know *what* it has! Because we were too confused! Mainly, we're *still* trying to figure out the plot of...

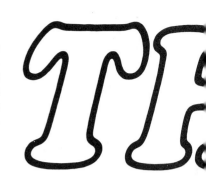

IE ZING

ARTIST: MORT DRUCKER   WRITER: ARNIE KOGEN

When last we saw the beloved Minestrone Family three years (and a couple of hundred bodies, and several Academy Awards, and $100 million in box office grosses) ago, God had made Vino, the original Odd Father, an offer he couldn't refuse and called him to that "Great Pizzeria In The Sky," and Micrin, Vino's youngest son, had taken over. We pick up the action again with Micrin Minestrone as Head of the Family and determined to prove that *he* can play . . .

THE O
PA

LAKE TAHOE, 1958

Gee, what a **great day!** Not a **cloud** in the sky!

Yeah! if it wasn't for them **letters** and **numbers** up there, the weather would be **perfect!**

Dummy! That sets the **time** and **place** of the **action!** See? We're at **Don Micrin Minestrone's estate** in Nevada for his son, **Antonio's, COMMUNION!**

What's a **Communion?**

It's like a **Bar Mitzvah** for **Catholics!**

Oh, yeah! A **Bar Mitzvah!** That's when a kid says a **prayer,** and then they give him a **fountain pen!** When does **Antonio** get the pen?

Probably in about **ten years** or so . . . unless he gets himself a real good **mouthpiece!**

Who's the **clown** who made the **rotten joke?**

That's **Rocco Mozzarella . . .** the **Capo** of **23 Mafia Families!**

Gulp! **Yeah?** Gee, he's a **witty guy!**

DD FATHER RT, TOO!

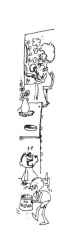

Panel 1 (left):

his **Communion** s wrecking my chedule, so I'll ave to **combine business** with **pleasure!** Now, id you **blow up** hose **three Las egas hotels** like told you, Tim?

Yes, it's been **taken care of!**

Good! Well, so much for **pleasure!** Now to **business!** What happened to the **Boy's Choir . . . ?**

Vinny **rubbed them out!**

My God! Give me **one** good reason **why!**

When somebody said the Choir was going to **sing . . .** Vinny thought it was to the **COPS!**

That's a good reason!

Panel 2 (right):

Micrin, all these people are waiting to kiss the Odd Father's hand and ask you for your **council**—or for a **favor!**

We go in **order of importance** —the **biggest crooks first!**

Sal Valducci! I'm in charge of **narcotics** in **New York!**

Sorry! Not big enough!

I'm **Frankie Jamminjelli** —a **Detroit Don!** I just had **46 men** wiped out!

Listen, everybody! I said the **BIGGEST CROOKS FIRST!!** Who are you . . . ?

I'm a **United States Senator!**

Now we're talking! **YOU'RE FIRST!**

ARTIST: MORT DRUCKER   WRITER: LARRY SIEGEL

Panel 3 (bottom left):

Mr. Minestrone, n your plan to **ake over** all of **as Vegas,** I've ot **news** for you!

Kiss my hand and **speak . . .**

I want **$250,000** . . . and a **piece** of the **action!**

Kiss my ass and **leave!**

I must see Micrin!

You'll have to wait in line like the **rest** of us, Lady!

I **can't believe** it! I'm **Number 62** in **line,** and I'm his **SISTER!**

What are **YOU** complaining about?!? I'm **Number 74,** and I'm his **WIFE!**

Panel 4 (bottom right):

Micrin . . . this is my **boy friend, Moil!** I'd like to **marry** him!

Him?!? This creep?! He's no **Husband** for an **Italian** girl! He's **not** one of **OUR KIND!**

But he **loves** me! He's **tender** and **gentle . . .** and he **never hits me!**

See? I TOLD you he's **not** one of our kind!

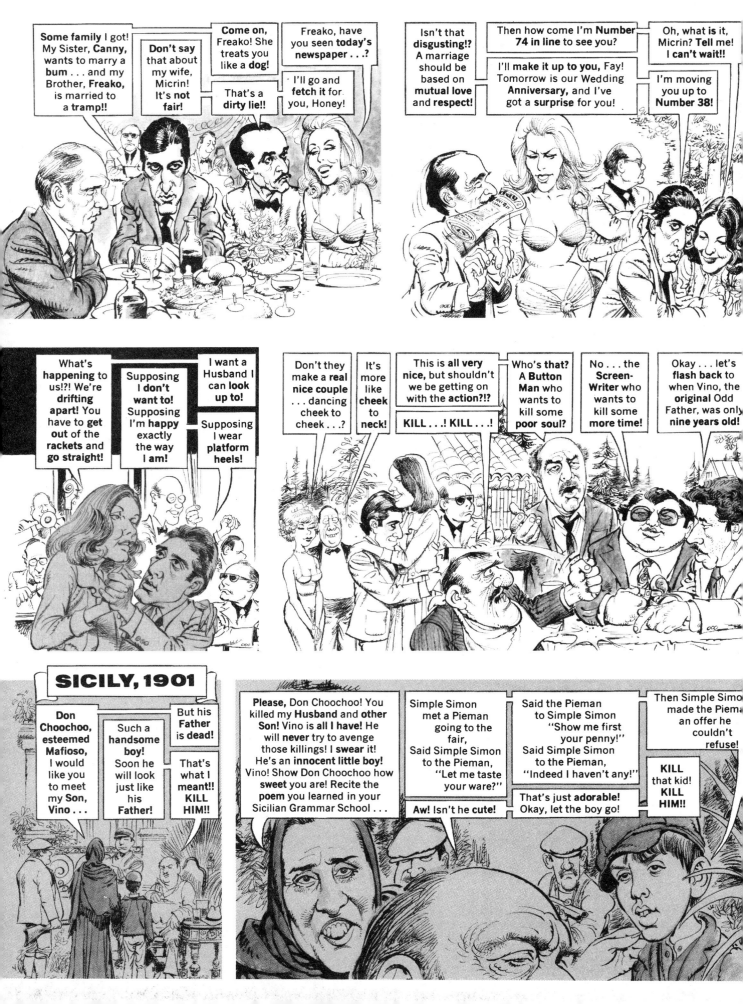

MIAMI BEACH, 1958

HAVANA, CUBA, 1958

LAKE TAHOE, 1959

It's **great** being **home**, Tim! But I **missed** being here for the **Holidays**! So give me a run-down! What did you get my Son, **Antonio**, as a **Christmas** present from me?

Detroit!

Kids nowadays are **spoiled rotten!** When **I** was a kid, the most **my** Father ever got me was **Staten Island!**

Well, **there** goes Freako! And there goes the hotel deal!

Hey, **everybody!** I think this is turning into a Surprise Party!

Oh, **yeah?** What's the **surprise?**

SURPRISE!!

And there goes the **country!**

WASHINGTON, D.C. 1959

Mr. Minestrone, you have been **called** before this Senate Committee because we are determined to **wipe out the cancer** that is threatening to **destroy America** in the '50's! State your **name** and **line of work** . . . and **no lying!**

I am **Micrin Minestrone!** I am the **Capo** of **Capos** in the Mafia! I control all **prostitution, gambling** and **narcotics** in this country. I deal in **extortion, blackmail** and **murder!** And I **won't** stop until the **whole world** is mine!

No . . . I **swear** it!

Thank you, and **God bless you!**

Mr. Minestrone, **stop stalling!** Are you **now,** or have you **ever** been a **Communist?**

Micrin, things are **piling up!** You got **scores** to settle with **Herman Roth** and **Freako** . . . and now a **Senate Investigating Committee** wants you to appear before them in **Washington!**

A Senate Committee? *Uh-oh!!* That could mean the **end** of our **whole operation!** By the way, **who owns** Washington?

Your **daughter, Maria!** You got it for **her** last Christmas!

I think we got a **fighting chance!**

NEW YORK CITY, 1917

What is the meaning of today's Religious Festival, Papa?

We are **grateful** that **we Italians** have lived through the **past year,** and we are asking the **Almighty** to please let us all live through the **coming year!**

And do you think that the Almighty . . . **Don Tuttifrutti** . . . WILL let us all live through the coming year, Papa?

Yes, if we give him a **little respect,** a **little devotion,** and a **lot of payola!**

Bless you, Don Tuttifrutti . . . **forever** and ever . . . Amen!

Hail, Don Tuttifrutti, our **Beloved Savior!**

Hey! How come **Vino Minestrone** is the **only** one around here who doesn't respect me? How come he doesn't offer **prayers** to me like the others?

But I **heard** him offer you a prayer a while ago!

Yeah? Well, you tell him that, **"Don Tuttifrutti, you're some cutie!"** is just **not good enough!**

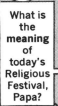

LAKE TAHOE, 1959

NEW YORK CITY, 1925

SICILY, 1925

LAKE TAHOE, 1959

CHINESE WATER TORTURE DEPT.

Recently, some of the big creative brains in Hollywood decided to revive the old-fashioned "Private Eye Mystery Movie!" At least, that's what the publicity releases about the picture say. Actually, the only old-fashioned things about this picture are the clothes and the cars! The rest is very "today" . . . complicated, long-winded and dull! And the hero? Well, he's a . . .

aclown

ARTIST: MORT DRUCKER   WRITER: LARRY SIEGEL

Let me explain the **movie business** to you! In the **old days, good stories** and **fine acting** were **important!** But today, it's **more** than that! Today, you **MUST** fill the screen with **40-year-old fashions, antique furniture** and **old cars!** Understand?

Sure! **I** get it! In other words, **today** people are paying **good money** for JUNK!!

Right!

But **this** film's gonna be **different!** It's gonna be a real old fashioned **"Private Eye Movie!"** It takes place in Los Angeles in the late 30's . . . and I'm **Joke Giddy, Private Eye!**

Big deal! If you're a **Private Eye,** what's your **gimmick?** All them old-fashioned shamuses had **shticks!**

I know! **Humphrey Bogart** owned **"tough"** . . . **William Powell** owned **"suave"** . . . **Brian Donlevy** owned **"short!"** So I needed something **NEW!** And here it is! **My** shtick is **"Snappy Dressing!"**

You've heard of the **"Fastest GUN in the West?"**

Mr. Giddy, I want you to get the goods on my **Husband!** He's fooling around with **another woman!** Perhaps you've **heard** of him—**Horace Mulebray,** the **Chief Engineer** with the **Los Angeles Water Dept.?**

Wow! A case dealing with the **Water Dept.** and **Reservoirs** and **Inside Doings** in the **City Government!** What a **dynamite plot** for a **Private Eye movie! William Powell** never had anything like it!

No . . . **DICK Powell** did! He solved it in a **Busby Berkeley Musical!**

As you can see, Los Angeles is in the midst of **severe water crisis!** There's nothing we can **do!** The city is in **trouble!**

We **can't!** We're operating on a **shoestring!** We have **no money, no material** and **no personnel!** We can't even build a **DAM!**

You're **exaggerating!** How about putting up **more reservoirs?!?**

Why **not?**

Our **beaver** is sick!

Now, **that's trouble!!**

DIATRIBAL LEGEND DEPT.

As long as I live, I'll **always remember** every second, every minute, every hour of those terrible days. It all started on a Saturday morning . . . no, it was a Sunday afternoon . . . maybe a Tuesday evening . . . anyway, it was in a remote part of New Mexico . . . or was it Arizona . . . or maybe it was Rhode Island . . . well, it was in **one** of those Western States! A gang of poachers were rounding up and shooting mustangs for dog food . . . or were they rounding up and shooting **dogs** for **mustang food**? Well, anyway, I'll **never forget** it . . .

Yahoo! Start shooting!

Whoopie! I haven't had this much fun since the hunting season opened on **Fawns** and **Puppies!**

Barnyard, I want you to become a **MAN** . . . so start shooting!

I can't shoot them, Pop! **I can't!** **I can't!**

Why not?

'Cause you **can't** shoot a **horse** in a movie!

Just make believe they're **Humans!**

Now, you're **talking!**

Hey, look who's **coming!** The cleanest living, most socially conscious man in the whole United States!

Really? What's **Dr. Marcus Welby** doing out here?

That's not Marcus Welby! That's . . .

BILLY JOCK

ARTIST: ANGELO TORRES   WRITER: STAN HART

Poser, I want you to **get off this land!**

Oh, **yeah?** How you gonna **make** me get off?

I **warn** you! I'm **slow** to **anger**— so I'm gonna count to **THREE!**

And **then** what?

And then I'm gonna count to **39,004!**

How come?

I just **TOLD** you!! I'm **slow** to anger!

Poser, pull that **trigger** . . . and you'll do something you'll **regret!**

What would I regret?

Making this into a **four** minute movie!

I see what you mean! Okay, men, let's go!

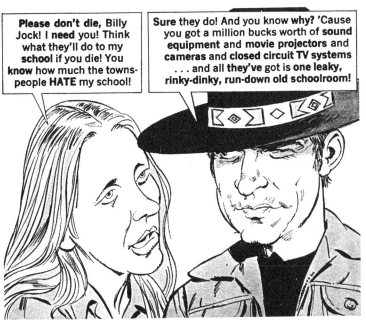

When you have problems and you don't want to think about them, what do you do? You go to the movies to take your mind off things, right? Wrong! Today, they're making movies that only *add* to your worries! Like—if you enjoy taking cruises, you can worry about dying in a "Poseidon Adventure"! Or if you live in the Los Angeles area, you can worry about dying in an "Earthquake"! Or, as is the case in this latest disaster epic, if you live or work in a modern, glass-walled skyscraper, you can worry about dying in—

Dug! How can you talk about moving out of the **city** after designing the **world's tallest building!** What could you possibly **do** out in the boondocks!

Design the world's tallest **outhouse!**

Do you have change for a **hundred dollar bill?**

Sure!

Er . . . do you have change for a **fifty?**

Why **not?!?**

Er . . . do you have change for a **dollar?**

Gee, I'm **sorry,** but I have **no** silver!

Too bad! I'll have to catch you **next** time around!

Holy cow! **138 floors!** I never saw a building **that** high in my **life!**

Neither did that **helicopter pilot!** He just crashed into the **side** of it!

THE TOWERING STERNO

ARTIST: MORT DRUCKER   WRITER: DICK DE BARTOLO

Ever see anything as **advanced** as this **Electronic Security System?** If anything goes **wrong** in the building, the computer knows about it **instantly!** It's an **absolutely perfect system!**

Er... Uh... It's a perfect system... with **one minor flaw!**

And when it **knows** something's wrong... how does it **tell us?**

Dug, that new **High-Rise** you designed in **Salt Lake City** is starting to **lean!**

Mr. Rivets, that reproduction of **The Leaning Tower of Pisa** that you designed for the new **World's Fair** is starting to **straighten up!**

Mr. Rivets, your **Fiancee's** in your **private office,** and she insists upon you seeing her **immediately!** I think it's an emergency **medical** problem!

What makes you say **that?**

She's **waiting** in **BED!**

Now look what you've done! You—you've caused a **short circuit!** Didn't I tell you not to plug any **heavy duty equipment** into this line?!

Heavy duty equipment...?! All I plugged in was my **electric razor!!**

Your **electric razor... AND** your **transistor radio!!** Just how much **overloading** do you think this building can **stand?!?**

This was so **clever** of you to have a **bed** installed in your office...

I figured the movie should start off with a **bang!**

By the way, I can't move out into the **sticks** with you! The **magazine** I work for finally gave me what I've **always wanted!**

What? An Executive Editor position?

No! A **better** "Route"... and a **brand new bicycle!**

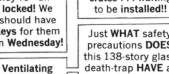

What building's on fire?

The Glassy Tower! It's on the 85th floor! Gee, I never fought a fire in a modern skyscraper building before! What's the first thing we do?

We wait till the fire burns down to the 5th floor . . . so we can reach it with our hoses!

Hi! I'm the Architect! Can I give you any vital information?

Does the building have a Sprinkler System . . . ?

Of course! And we expect to connect it up with the water supply next week!

How about Fire Exits?

Two on every floor! But they're—uh—locked! We should have keys for them on Wednesday!

Ventilating System . . . ?

Definitely On every floor . . . in packing crates . . . waiting to be installed!!

Just WHAT safety precautions DOES this 138-story glass death-trap HAVE at this moment?!?

Well . . . we've installed "NO SMOKING" signs in each and every elevator!

Dodger, did you change any of Dug Rivets' original electrical specifications?

Sure I did! When you ordered me to shave 4 million dollars off the budget for the building, did you ever ask me HOW I did it? Did you ever wonder WHY our monthly electric bill for all 138 stories is only $6.00?

Well, I'll TELL you! This entire building is plugged into the lamppost on the corner!

Do you think anyone suspects we're having an affair?

Nahh! As far as everyone is concerned, you're just my secretary working from 9 to 5!

Yes . . . but working from 9 at night to 5 in the morning might arouse SOME suspicion!

Did you leave a cigar burning?

I don't think so, especially since I don't smoke cigars! I'll go check!

Was I right? Did someone leave a cigar burning?

No . . . a cigarette! A KING SIZE one! But, don't worry!! I'll call for help!

HELP! HELP!

Wouldn't you get more response if you said that into the PHONE?

Not with the phone service in THIS building! HELP . . . ! !

They sure are calling out the equipment for this fire! What company are you guys with . . . ?

The 122nd Battalion!

That's a long way from downtown San Francisco, isn't it?

I'd say so! We're based in New York City!

Please, folks! Please! No **pushing**! No **shoving**! There's room for **eleven people** in that elevator!

But the **sign** says the elevator holds **TWELVE**!

That's **right**! It holds eleven people . . . and **ME**!! So, please— no **pushing**!! No **shoving**!!

The **Fire Door** is **jammed shut**! Isn't there supposed to be a **Fire Axe** for **just such** an emergency?

Sure! It's located just on the **other side** of the Fire Door!

C'mon! Help me go through the **building** and arouse all the **Tenants**!

That . . . and also to see if we can collect **next month's rent** in advance!

Hey, must you wear that **radio** throughout the entire picture?

To warn them about the **fire**?

I **do**, if I want to hear some **ENTERTAINMENT**!

We'll be **safe** going down these **Fire Stairs** . . . except that I **DO** think I smell **leaking gas**! I'll light a **match** and see if I can tell where it's **coming** from—

BOOM!

Good work, Mr. Rivets! You sure found that **gas leak**! You may know a lot about **electricity**, but you know **beans** about **gas**!

Okay! We've got to **keep walking down**! And you'll notice that, to **join** me, all you have to **take** is **ONE STEP**! So I suggest you **close your eyes** . . . because that **one step** is now **four stories high**!

Behind this panel is a **shaft** that runs the length of the building! I already **GOT** the shaft **ONCE** . . . when I agreed to **do** this movie!

Now I'm going to get it **again** . . . when I **use** it to climb up to the **party** in the **Marmalade Room** . . .

So while I'm **gone**, Fullip, I want you to act like an **adult**! Do you know what **that** means?

Yeah . . . I should **cry** and **yell** and **scream** and **carry on** a lot!

Gee, but that's **thoughtful**! Here we are, in the middle of a **holocaust** . . . and the kitchen sends up an elevator full of **barbecued beef**!

Man, **that's no barbecued beef**! Unless they've **dressed it** in the **clothes** the people who just went **DOWN** in the elevator were wearing!

You— you mean those are members of the **CAST?!?**

Boy, I've heard of being **roasted** by the **Critics** . . . but **this** is **ridiculous**!

The elevator's gone! I'm taking the Fire Exit!

My Agent said the same thing, but I'm going anyway!

The Fire Chief said there is no way out . . . !

Go ahead! Make an ASH of yourself!

FIRE EXIT

You're back! You couldn't make it . . . could you!?!

Of course I could have! It's just that I felt guilty leaving you here!

Omolette, I have a confession to make! I came here tonight to sell you 1000 shares of a phony oil stock! But now that we've met, I— I just can't do it!

I've always said I know an honest man when I see one!

Er—how do you feel about buying 2000 shares of a phony gold mining stock?

And I think I see one, way— way— over there!

Look! Helicopters! They're going to evacuate you folks from the roof!!

Oh, thank God for American ingenuity!

It's five bucks for each kid, ten bucks for each adult, and $18.50 for a couple! You . . . er . . . still feel that way about American ingenuity!

How's the evacuation from the roof going?

No one has left yet!

Gee! I thought the rates were reasonable! Do you think we should offer group discounts?

No, the rates were fine! It's just too windy to land up there!

Then the only way to move people out is by a breeches buoy strung across the way to the Fearless Building! See if the helicopter can get a good strong line into the Marmalade Room!

If they can, it'll be the first good strong line in this entire picture!

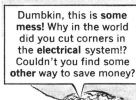
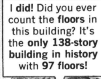

I know you're supposed to break a window so the helicopter can get a line in here, but why are you smashing ALL of the windows?

Busting windows is like eating potato chips, Lady! Smash one —and you gotta smash 'em all!

Dumbkin, this is some mess! Why in the world did you cut corners in the electrical system!? Couldn't you find some other way to save money?

I did! Did you ever count the floors in this building? It's the only 138-story building in history with 97 floors!

Okay, here's the line from the helicopter! Pull it in! C'mon, men! Pull . . . pull! That's the way! And here's the other end! The end that was supposed to be attached to the building across the way! Er . . . that was a little too much pulling, men!

Will you tell me why we're here . . . placing explosives on these tanks?

There are **two million gallons of water** in these tanks! We're going to **blow them up**, so the water will **pour down through the building** and put out this **blasted fire!**

Sure! And **while** all that water is pouring down through the building, putting out the fire, it's **also** going to **DROWN** everyone!!

Sorry about that! It's **my** job to **put out fires** and **save people** from **burning to death!** If you want to save people from **drowning**, call in the **Coast Guard!**

BLAM! BOOM! CHOOM!

Here comes the water!

The fire is OUT! The fire is OUT!!

Big deal!! I can't swim!!

And I'm being washed out of the windo-o-o . . .

And I've got a ten-ton BEAM on my stomach!

We were better off with the FIRE!

It's a miracle . . . a miracle!

That we're all still alive?

No, that we're **all down here on the street** when, **twenty minutes ago**, there wasn't an **elevator** working or a **stairway** standing! I sure wish I knew how we **did** it!

You guys will keep making these fire-traps **higher** and **higher**, and I'll keep eating **smoke** until somebody asks **ME** how to build them **RIGHT!**

Okay, **I'M asking!** My new building has a **seven million dollar budget** for **Fire Safety Equipment** . . . and **every** dollar you **save**, you can **keep!**

Well, **first of all**, **why** do we need **Fire Axes** and Sprinklers on **every floor!** Every **OTHER** floor is **plenty!** So what if you have to **walk up** a few steps!? And also . . .

All we can do is pray to God that we can **stop** this kind of terrible thing from **ever happening again!**

You mean **another fire** like this??

No, **another MOVIE** like this! How **many** disasters can we **take?**

FROM "SOUP" TO "NUTS" DEPT.

Every once in a while, a motion picture comes along that exhilarates the sense, expands the imagination, and explores the unknown. Unfortunately, this is not o of those movies! The only new technique this movie employs is to have the acto all speak their lines at the same time. MAD applauds said new technique in th movie. The stars don't have to know their lines well, and the audience hears a that boring dialogue in ⅓ the normal time. And when all that pseudo-scienti mumbo-jumbo and all those drug trips are thrown at you, the film leaves you in

ASSAULTED STATE

ARTIST: ANGELO TORRES   WRITER: DICK DE BARTOLO

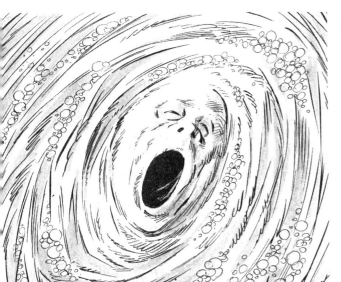

For a while there, we were being treated to a rash of bank robbery films in which the criminals were clever, their plans ingenious and the execution brilliant. However, we are now threatened with a new, sickening trend in bank robbery films . . . inspired by the success of this latest farce . . . in which the criminals are IDIOTS who get themselves all loused up one hot

DUM-DU

M AFTERNOON

ARTIST: MORT DRUCKER   WRITER: LARRY SIEGEL

Okay! **One false move,** and I'll fill you full . . . of . . . **BUDS!!**

Hey! What's **going on** here?!? Sap, I told you a **thousand times,** "Put **the gun** in the **flower box!** Put the **gun** in the flower **box!**" What did you do with the **gun?!?**

Promise you **won't** get **mad,** Funny?

Promise!

I . . . I put it in a **pitcher of water** on the **kitchen table!**

AAARRGH!

Funny, you **PROMISED!!**

No . . . I **don't** think that's **The Godfather!**

I guess not!

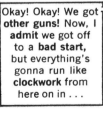

Okay! Okay! We got **other guns!** Now, I **admit** we got off to a **bad start,** but everything's gonna run like **clockwork** from here on in . . .

You guys'll **never get away with this!**

Oh, **no?** Hey, Mac, y'know who we **are?** We are two **Vietnam War veterans!** We are **not afraid** of anything! This is gonna be a **smooth, efficient, well-oiled operation** . . .just the way us **Americans** handled the **War in Vietnam!**

Wait! Let me put it **another** way . . .

Okay! Now for the first **step** in our **Master Plan** . . .

What are you **doing?**

What d'ya **think** I'm doing? **Spraying** the **TV cameras!**

With **DEODORANT SPRAY?!?** That won't knock 'em out! They'll **STILL** photograph everything!

I know that, dummy! But you gotta admit they're gonna sure **smell nice!** If there's one thing I can't stand, it's a **smelly TV camera!**

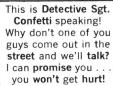

Driving The Golden Spike

Scenes We'd Like to See

FLEE CIRCUS DEPT.

Years ago there was a hit TV show about a man always on the move, hounded and persecuted endlessly and living the life of a forlorn nomad—but enough about Gomer Pyle! We're talking about Dr. Richard Cornball, a man with the cunning, intelligence and resourcefulness of three men! Unfortunately, those three men happen to be Moe, Larry and Curly (and occasionally Shemp or Joe Besser!), which is why we call him...

Forgive me for being **overbearing**, but as **Police Chief**, I **have** to ask **probing questions**! Besides, I **like** being overbearing! Now, **tell me your story**!

I'm **Doctor Richard Cornball**! I came **home** and found my **wife** on the **floor** with the **phone in her hand**! I find her that way **every night** but tonight was **different**! She was also **dead**! There was a **man** in the room! He had **one arm**! I know, because he said it was **chilly out** and wanted to borrow **one glove**! He got **away**! I **ran** after him but he was **too fast**! If only he had **one leg** instead of **one arm**! I've **told you** all this a **dozen times**!

We **know**! But for the **three** people who **didn't** see the **TV series** that lasted four years, and the **two** people who didn't see the **hit movie**, we have to **re-establish** the **ridiculous plot**!

GOTTA RUN...!

Did your wife ever mention **anyone threatening** her? Any **odd** phone calls? Any **disturbing** letters?

Just the **one** from *Publisher's Clearing House*! My wife was **upset** when I told her **all** their **envelopes** say "You're a **$10 million winner**!"

Every envelope says that? **Damn**, I just gave my **30 day notice**! I thought I was going to be **rich enough to retire**!

If a guy with a **fake** hand **killed** your **wife**, how come we **didn't find** any **fake fingerprints**?

Certainly you can do some more **investigating**!

Just to save **your life**? We have more **important** things to do! There are cars **double parked** all over **Chicago** that need to be **ticketed**!

And I **just ticketed yours**, **Cornball**! Doctor's plates **don't mean** @#*&% around here!

THE STOOGE-ITIVE

ARTIST: ANGELO TORRES   WRITER: DICK DEBARTOLO

Listen up! There's a **fugitive** on the **run!** I want a **thorough search** of the **entire area!** Look behind **every tree, every rock, every blade of grass!**

Every blade of **grass?** The escapees are **over six feet** tall!

Then just **look** behind **every tall blade** of **grass!**

One of them was a **doctor!** Should I **check** the local **hospitals?**

Sure, as long as you're **not** in an **HMO!** Then you'll **never find** the **doctor** you're **looking for!**

Damn, I **can't believe** the paperwork **Blue Cross** and **Blue Shield** require! And this is just for when you **break** into a **hospital** and **treat yourself!**

BLUE CROSS DOES NOT COVER SHAVES OR HAIRCUTS.

MOSQUITO HOST

Doctor, you may have **escaped** from us at the **hospital,** and you may have **escaped** from us at the **tunnel,** but there's **no way** you're **escaping** from us **now!** You can **surrender peacefully or die!**

Dive? Hey, **thanks a lot** for the **advice!**

Damn, I said **"die,"** not **"dive!"** Why'd I **open** my **big mouth?**

Let's **call off** the **search!** No one could **survive** a **dive** from **that height!**

I **don't** take **chances!** I want **road blocks** and **bridge blocks!** And a **set** of **blocks** for me to **play with** while they're setting them up! I want **heli-copters, police cars** and **artillery!** I want **guard dogs** downstream, **guard cats** upstream and **guard fish** in the water! And I want **dramatic music** playing **throughout!**

I'M FOR GUN CONTROL

Dr. Cornball **survived** the **dive** from the top of the **dam** and **escaped** from the **river,** but we **lucked out!** We **know** where **he is!**

Really? What **clued you in?**

Something **we heard** in the **background** while he was making his phone call! **Listen!**

WANTED FOR ARSON

Hey **mac,** when are you gonna **get off** that phone—**hey, I recognize you!** You're Doctor Cornball, the **murderer!** Can you beat that? **Dr. Cornball,** wearing a **brown jacket** and **tan chino pants,** using a **payphone** at the **corner** of **State** and **3rd Street!** At **9:29 A.M.!**

Cornball got **away** from me **two more** times! And now he's **disappeared** into the **St. Patrick's Day Parade!** I can't believe his **luck!**

Neither can I! **Saint Patrick's Day** was a **week ago!** He's **lucky** the **Irish** people in **Chicago** like **long parties!**

Fellow doctors, I am so **proud** to have lead the research for **DD7**, otherwise known as **Profane!** It has **no side effects** whatsoever!

You know that's **not true**, Dr. Nicotine! **Profane** does tremendous **liver** damage, **lung** damage, **brain** damage, and **worst** of all it results in **hair** with **split ends!**

Well…er…**that's** all **true**, but when I said **Profane** has no **side** effects, I meant it never **affects** a patient's **side!** And I'm talking about **both** the **left side** and the **right side!**

And you **doctored** the research, **doctor!** You **didn't** use the **liver** samples **I** sent you! You **didn't** even use **human** livers! You used **Alpo** liver chunks! Right from the **can!**

Human liver? **Alpo** liver? Stop **nit-picking!** Come on Dr. Cornball, **step out** on the **terrace** and let's talk about this!

This building **has no terrace!**

Again with the **nit-picking!**

Tell the Chicago Police **not** to **shoot** them!

Why **not?**

I did all the **running** to get them! **I deserve** to **shoot** them!

Dr. Cornball, give **yourself** up! I **know** you **didn't kill** your **wife!** And I **know** about the **one-armed man!** And I **know** about the **liver samples!** And I **know** Dr. Nicotine killed your **wife!** And I **know** it was because of **kickbacks** from the **drug conglomerate!** I've **known everything** for about a **month** now!

Why didn't you **mention** any of this **earlier?**

I needed the **overtime!** You rich **doctors** don't **know** what it's like living on a **cop's** salary!

If you'd like to **arrest** the **one-armed man**, you'll find him on the **el train!** I **handcuffed** him to a **pole** in one of the **cars!**

That explains **this!** Unfortunately, you **handcuffed** his **fake arm** to a pole! He got away and he's probably **gunning** for **you** right **now!**

OH NO! HERE WE GO AGAIN!

RAIDERS OF THE LOST ARM

SAIGON HILTON

You are about to see a **very important picture** about the **War in Vietnam!** It begins here in **Saigon** . . . and I'm **Captain Benjamin Dullard,** waiting for re-assignment!

As you **know,** this conflict is **costing** the United States **billions of dollars!** After all, **WE** have a commitment . . . to take care of the **people** of South Vietnam!

A Croc

GO HOME

Before I give you your **new assignment,** Captain, tell me more about your **combat experience!**

Well, General, in **'70** I fought for **8 months** in the jungles outside **Saigon!** In '69, I went on **98 chopper missions,** and killed hundreds of—

You call **THAT combat?** Why you ☆⑥❊!✆★ **goldbrick,** you don't know the **first thing** about combat!

In **'69,** I was stationed in **Chicago,** when the **Hippies** attacked the **Democratic Convention!**

You **poor kid!** You **HAVE** been through Hell!

Your assignment is to **find Col. Klutz!** Here is an old **picture** of him, and I want you to listen to a **recent tape** of what we **THINK** is his **voice** . . .

I spent **YEARS** out here, fighting the Cong! And they **always** wanted to give me **MEDALS!**

We **BELIEVE** it's his voice! We're not sure!

But I told them **I NEVER ACCEPT** awards! You guys want to give me an award, give it to some **INDIAN broad!**

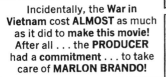

Incidentally, the **War in Vietnam** cost **ALMOST** as much as it did to **make this movie!** After all . . . the **PRODUCER** had a **commitment** . . . to take care of **MARLON BRANDO!**

As I think back to the **beginning** of this long struggle, I remember things like our **high purpose,** our **noble ideals,** and our great desire to **save Southeast Asia** from the **brutal oppression of Communism!** Of course, in **retrospect,** that's all . . .

K.O' **BLIP!** NOW

WRITER: LARRY SIEGEL

That's **HIM,** General! Take my **word** for it! I just **KNOW** it's him!

Col. Klutz was once a **great soldier,** but the war's made him **psycho!** Right now, he's running his **own army** under his **own rules!** He **thinks** he's **GOD!** You can see how **sick** and **twisted** his **mind** is . . .!

I'm **sure** God will **FORGIVE** him for that!

I **WILL NOT!!**

Your job is to **track down** Colonel Klutz in **Cambodia,** infiltrate his **army,** and **ELIMINATE** him!! You think you have the **STOMACH** for that sort of thing, Capt.?

No problem, Sir! Many times I've seen my men kill a **HUMAN ANIMAL** who was **threatening** the **American Way of Life!**

I'm talking about an **Officer** of the **U.S. Army!**

So am I . . .!

Scenes We'd Like to See

The Human Shield

There are hundreds of thousands of U.S. Marines dedicated to Unit, Corps, God and Country! In any group that large it's not surprising to find...

ARTIST: MORT DRUCKER

A FEW GOOFY MEN

I'm **Lt. Colonel Marksman!** People say working for **Colonel Fessup** is **very tough** but we get on **fine!** I just lie, **cheat** and **steal** to **cover his ass,** kind of like what **Bush** did for **Reagan!**

I'm **Lt. Can-trick** and I think **Colonel Fessup** is **brilliant** too! People ask me if I think the **Colonel** ever makes a mistake! That's **crazy!** Does **God** make **mistakes? Of course He does!** But **Colonel Fessup? Never!**

I'm **Corporal Lance Darwin** and this is my buddy, **Dummy.** I'm his **idol** and we're an **inseparable team!** If I get a **cold, HE sneezes. I feel bad** for him—last time **I had** food poisoning **HE threw up** for **three days!**

I've got some **bad news** for you, **buddy!** I've been **limping** lately— you better get **checked** out for a **hernia!**

I'm the **judge,** and this is a very **difficult case— not difficult** to judge **who's right,** diffi- cult to keep from **laughing** at all the **stupidity** that goes on in my **courtroom!**

REQUEST FOR TRANSFER: Carmine T. Sandiego (SCREW UP)

WRITER: DICK DEBARTOLO

I'd like to talk to you about **Darwin** and **Dummy,** the **two** marines you're **defending!**

Oh **them?** They'll be in **prison** for **two** to **four years!**

You **haven't talked** to a **single witness,** haven't heard a **single fact,** and you **know the outcome?**

I don't mess up my cases with **meaningless inci- dentals** like **writs** and **witnesses!** It's **stupid procedures** like that that tie up our **court system!**

You're **abso- lutely nothing** like your **famous father!**

In- deed, that's **very true!** He's **dead!**

And he's still **more animated** than you! One thing's **for sure,** he wasn't **a screw-up** like **you** are! I bet you **don't even know** where the **courtroom is!**

I **do so!** I just **don't know** what I'm **supposed to do** should I ever **get inside!**

PLAY BALL!

My **clients** won't **plea bargain,** so we're going to **court!** I have a **vague feeling** we're going to **lose** this **case!**

You're so **wishy washy! Nothing** like your **father!** He **believed** in **his convictions!**

You're **right!** I **don't** have a **vague** feeling we're going to **lose the case!** I'm **absolutely sure** we're going to **lose!**

That's better!

These are the **facts** of the case! Listen **carefully!** Marine officers **Darwin** and **Dummy** broke into the barracks of **PFC Carmine Sandiego** and **murdered him!** It's **that simple!** But my **legal opponent** will try to sway you from that with **misdirection, unqualified witnesses** and **incredible overacting!** And he will **dazzle you** with **official sounding terms** like **"latrine"**—but don't **fall** for his **theatrics!**

Contrary to what **my opponent** has said, my defense will be **straightforward** and **untheatrical!** Now watch me **pull a witness** out of **my hat!**

So I can **establish your credentials** as a **doctor,** let me ask you **this:** How much do **two aspirins cost** when **billed** through a **health insurance company?**

$200!

Okay, now we **know** we're dealing with a **medical expert!** Doctor, what would you say to a man who started **coughing up blood?**

Gesundheit! And would you please **cover your mouth!**

I call a **recess!** I've never quite seen a **circus like this!** I've got to **confer** with an **expert,** Judge Wapner!

I didn't mean to **startle you,** but I had to **come forward** with the **truth!** I signed **Sandiego's** transfer **five days** after he **died!**

Five days? So it was a **cover-up!**

Sort of…I mean, you know how the government loves **red tape!** If I had **rushed** I might have been able to sign his transfer **only two days** after he **died!**

This is a **break** for me! **Marksman,** you're a **valuable witness,** so I'm going to **watch after** you in the **sleaziest motel in town!**

I've got **Marksman,** and I'm **putting** him on the **bench!**

Bench? You mean the **stand,** idiot! If you go after the **Colonel,** you could be **court martialed** for pro**fessional misconduct!**

I got you there, **boss!** There's **nothing professional** about my **conduct!**

Scenes We'd Like to See

The Big Break

A talented writer named Steven King once wrote a terrifying book called "The Shining." Now, a famous Director named Stanley Kubrick has made a movie out of it. Unfortunately, his film has given Mr. King's book, and all the other great horror films of the past, a black eye! Which is why we at MAD call our version:

SHiNER

Our hotel **closes** for the **winter** in a few days, and we like to have someone around to keep an **eye** on it until **spring**, when **we re-open!** Have you had any **experience** as a **HOTEL-SITTER,** Mr. Torrents . . . ?

Plenty! I sat for a few **Holiday Inns,** a couple of **Hiltons,** and just recently I sat for **Caesars Palace** in Las Vegas!

Hey, **wait a minute! CEASARS PALACE NEVER CLOSES!!**

It DID THEN! It was the week **McLEAN STEVENSON** was appearing there . . . !

He cleared out the whole hotel?!?

The **hotel,** the **entire state,** and **three border towns** in Arizona!

You've **got** yourself a **job!** You **know,** of course, that it's **lonely** in an empty hotel! I hope you have **enough** to keep yourself **occupied!**

Yes! I'm a **writer!**

Oh? What are you **working** on?

A **new** TV sit-com series for **McLean Stevenson!** The way I figure . . . that should clear out the **Network!!**

Ah-hah! So when you're **finished here,** you can **sit** for **NBC!** I like a man who **plans** for the **future!**

ARTIST: ANGELO TORRES

WRITER: LARRY SIEGEL

I'll go pick up my **wife** and **son** and be here on Friday!

Wonderful! And . . . please! **Ignore** all those rumors you keep hearing about this hotel being **weird** and **haunted!**

I will! Oh, by the way . . . who's **HE??**

He's our **Night Clerk!** It's a **thankless job** being on duty **all night long,** but **he** seems to **love** it!!

I'm not too crazy about this **job,** Wack!

Aw, **c'mon,** Windy! We're gonna have a **terrific winter!**

But we've **done** it all **before!** Sitting around a hotel day after day after day . . . **BORING** each other to death!!

You know . . . you're **right!** It **WILL** be just like a **SECOND HONEYMOON!**

Okay, Son, now **you** tell me all about what's **troubling** you . . . and **Daddy** will **help** you!

Daddy, you got a **strange look** in your eyes! Are you gonna **hurt** me and Mommy?

HURT you?! Why should I **HURT** you?! You're **my FAMILY**, and I **LOVE** my family! Just like I love the family **I** come from!

WHAT family is **THAT**, Daddy . . . ?

The "Charles Manson" family!

REDRUM
SERUTAN
YRRAB NODNYL

ON-THE-SPOT GRAFFITI

Now, **let's** clear up this silly business about room 238! I **assure** you, there's **nothing unusual** in here . . .

See? I told you there's nothing un- usual here!

But, **Daddy!** Look . . . !! **LOOK** . . . !!

Son, **trust me!** This happens in **EVERY** hotel when a **guest** waits for a **Bell Hop** to come up and help him down with his luggage!

See . . . ? There was **nothing** to worry about! Now, **you** go back to **Mommy**, and **I'm** going to stop off at the **Bar** for a few drinks . . . !

But, **Daddy!** The **Bar** is **CLOSED!** Didn't Mr. Ulpman tell us we're the **only ones here** and there's **no liquor** in the hotel?

Dinny, I happen to know for a **fact** they **serve spirits** in here!

Gee, Daddy . . . are you **SURE??**

BIER AND AIL
DIE IT SODA
VERY BLOODY MARY
STIFF DRINKS
CHARGE IT

The BOOM BOOM ROOM
Red SKELETON

Shweeet Ad—oh—line! My Ad—oh—line . . . !!

Son, **trust me again!!**

Welcome to the **Fantasy Bar**, Mr. Torrents! I am your **phantom bartender**, Floyd . . . and I hope you enjoy your **make-believe drinks!** You see, **everything** here is imaginary . . .

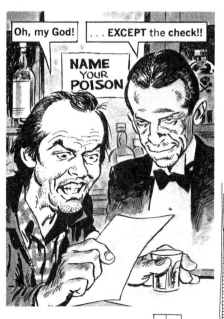

Oh, my God!

. . . **EXCEPT** the check!!

NAME YOUR POISON

Scenes We'd Like to See

The Doctor's Pronouncement.

WRITER: AL JAFFEE

ARTIST: MORT DRUCKER

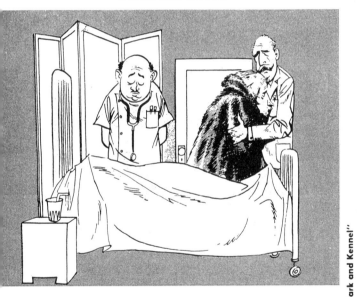

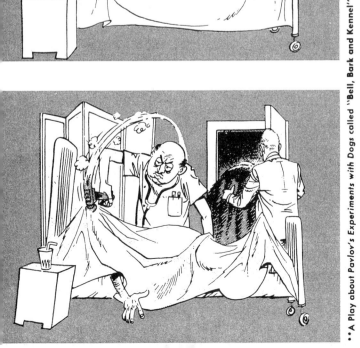

**A Play about Pavlov's Experiments with Dogs called "Bell, Bark and Kennel"

No matter what kind of role he plays, Steve McQueen is always Steve McQueen! He was Steve McQueen when he did his *sailor bit* in "The Sand Pebbles"! He was Steve McQueen when he did his *illegitimate father bit* in "Love With A Proper Stranger"! He was Steve McQueen when he did his *sophisticated crook bit* in "The Thomas Crown Affair"! And if you've seen his latest...in which he plays a detective, then you'll have to agree that he's still Steve McQueen, even when he does his...

"BULLBIT"

ARTIST: MORT DRUCKER   WRITER: AL JAFFEE

Lieutenant Bullbit? My name is **Walter Charmless!** I'm an ambitious politician! I asked your Chief to send me the best man on the force! I've got an assignment that requires the utmost skill, intelligence, patience and alertness...but it **also** requires one other thing that's **more important** than all the rest... and that is that you **stay awake** while I'm **talking** to you!

He **IS** awake, Mr. Charmless! That's just Steve McQueen's way of **underplaying** his role! He's acting **real cool!**

Snoring is acting **real cool??** Anyway, here is your assignment: **Johnny Thug** has quit the **Mafia** and is **ready to talk!** I want you to keep him alive until **Monday** so he can testify before my **Investigating Committee** ...thereby catapulting me into prominence as the **greatest "Crime-Buster"** this nation **has ever had!** But I must **warn** you . . .

Failure will bring you **certain death!**

You mean from the **Mafia . . .?**

No, I mean from **ME!!** Nobody's gonna louse up **MY** chance to be the greatest "Crime-Buster" this nation has ever had!!

Okay, Mr. Charmless, where **IS** this Mafia hood we're supposed to guard?

As you know . . . in current movies, the accent is on **credibility** and **realism!** With this in mind, where's the **FIRST** place the Mafia would **look** for him? In some **sleazy skid row flop house**, right? And where's the **LAST** place they'd look? In some plush hotel like **this** one, right?

Right! What room is he in?

307 . . . in the **Hotel Sleazy!** That's a **skid row flop house** across town! I said the accent was on **credibility** and **realism!** I **never** said anything about **LOGIC!**

So get over there and **start baby–sitting** this guy! By the way, Sgt—I think your friend is **underplaying** again!

No...this time he's **really ASLEEP!** In fact, considering how **dull** this dialogue's been so far, it's a wonder **ANY** of us are still awake!!

43

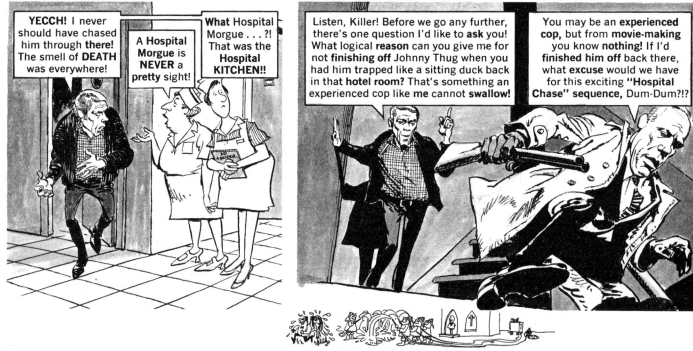

MAVERSHTICK

ARTIST: MORT DRUCKER   WRITER: ARNIE KOGEN

What an **entrance!** Coming into town with a **jackass!**

Yeah! It sure must be **humiliating** for that **poor mule!**

That's **Brat Mavershtick!** He's supposed to be **tough!**

Yeah? He doesn't **look** as **tough** as **Billy the Kid!**

Hell, he doesn't **look** as **tough** as **Billy Crystal!**

They say **Mavershtick's** the **quickest** in the **west!**

The **quickest draw?**

The **quickest one-liner shooter!**

That's just what we **need** around here— **ranchers, settlers,** and **wannabe frontier stand-up comics!**

WHITEFISH WILL

DOWN WITH DRUGS DOWN WITH ALCOHOL DOWN WITH BROTHELS

My name is **Mangle,** and I'm so **tough** I swallow **razor blades** so I can **shave** my **beard** from the **inside!** Whatta ya got to say about **that,** Mavershtick?

There's a **stage leaving** at eight tomorrow! **Be under it!**

Wow! He **is quick! I didn't** see that **one-liner coming!**

Mind if I **sit in** on this **game?**

We're playing **five-card draw!** I hear **your specialty** is **stud!**

That's true! But when it comes to **poker,** I'm a **five-card coward!** And I promise to **lose** for an **hour!**

Sounds **good** to me! Have a **seat!**

9

One of the year's biggest movies is about a group of pinheaded scientists who ran around Oklahoma chasi
tornadoes with all the frenzy of Marlon Brando at an all-you-can-eat Polynesian buffet! Why they were trying
catch up with a deadly, whirling cone of air, debris and assorted bovines is too confusing to be explained in
200-page science book, much less this intro! It begs the question: "Who are the bigger schmucks — the id
scientists, or the dolts who paid eight bucks to see this dreck?" Hmmm...let's face it, we're ALL a bunch o

UMA THURMAN: Tall, Nordic-looking film actress...or what *everyone's* name sounds like after a dentist's appointment?

CHE GUEVARA: Latin American revolutionary...or trendy Beverly Hills eatery with valet parking and $45 margaritas?

MUCHO DE NIRO DEPT.

For as long as we can remember, the plot of a "Fight Picture" was usually very simple. An underprivileged kid starts in the gutter, and blasts his way to the top. Then, along comes the first major Fight Picture of the '80's, and what do we get: an underprivileged kid starts in the gutter, and blasts his way to the sewer! Boy, Hollywood has given us our fair share of "anti-heroes" in the past, but now make way for the "anti-anti-anti hero" affectionately known as the . . .

RAVI

Wow! This is the greatest fight of 1941!

Look at that! A **White** man and a **Black** man, together in the **same** ring, beatin' each other's **brains** out!

Yeah! **Who said** integration would never work!?

That **Jerk LaMutha ain't HUMAN**! He's **never** been knocked off his **feet**!!

He's **never BEEN** off his feet —period!! He even **SLEEPS standing up**!!

Are you **sure?!?** Only **horses** sleep standing up!

Trust me! He once spent two weeks in my **stable**!

They **promised** me a **crack** at **LaMutha**, but **first** I gotta win a couple of **real easy warm-up** fights!

Yeah . . . ? With **who**?

The **Japs** and the **Nazis**!

Kill the friggin' bum, Jerk! Hit the frig right in his friggin' **mouth**!!

ARTIST: MORT DRUCKER

I can't believe it, Shmoey! It —it's my **first** loss! I dropped the **decision**!!

Big deal! So you lost! You gotta act like a **MAN**! You gotta do what's **expected** of you!

I guess you're right!

Okay! Now beat up the Referee and the two Judges and let's go!

What's wrong with **Jerk** these days, Shmoey?

Why? He's his **usual self**! Mean, rotten, foulmouthed and disgusting!

Yeah?!? How come he won't let the **Mob** buy into him? Why won't he **throw fights**?

Okay!! **Okay**!! Gee . . . I **never** said he was **PERFECT**

NG BULLY

I've never heard such language in my entire life!!

"Friggin'" is dirty?! They use worse language than that on **Saturday Morning TV Cartoons!**

For **MAD Magazine** it's dirty! Remember the **good old days** when MAD used to use "✳⑥☆ⓒ◌!★" instead of curse words! They've sure come a **long way!!**

Using **"friggin' "** instead of ☆⑥◌!⌾★⑥ is **some long way!** On a flight from **New York** to **L.A.,** that's like a **forced landing** in Jersey City!!

Hey, Jerk!! **Destroy** the friggin' bum!

Tear the friggin' crud apart!!

FRIGGIN'! FRIGGIN'! That's all I **hear! Enough** already with that **vile, disgusting** word!!

KILL the @ # & + % $ @ + bum! Knock his @ # $ % &! **head** off!!

Hey, who are you?!

The **Editor** of MAD Magazine . . . just taking a little trip down **Memory Lane!!**

I'M THE CHAMP! I'M THE CHAMP!

I COULDA BEEN A CONTENDER!

WRITER: LARRY SIEGEL

Of all the guys in The Bronx, I had to marry **you!** Look at you! **You** ain't a **man!** You're an **animal!!**

An **animal?!** Hey, you friggin' broad! Don' **ever** call me an animal **again!** I may be just a **pug,** but I got **pride** and **dignity!** I ain't no **animal!!**

Okay! **Okay!** Now . . . **how** do you want your **meat . . . ? Raw,** as usual?!?

Yeah! With maybe a li'l **Gravy Train** on the **side!**

Okay, here's your **meat,** Meat Head!

You call this **RAW?!?** Here's a **KNUCKLE SANDWICH** for **YOUR** supper!!

Hey, you two! What's goin' **ON** up there?

I'LL tell you what's goin' on here, fight fans! **Jerk** lands a **left** to the **eye** an' the **broad** counters with a **hard right** to the **ribs!** Two quick **jabs** from **Jerk** sends her **reeling,** an' he closes in for the **finish!** Her legs are **wobbly!** She's **down!!**

I **STILL** think she's foolin' aroun'! Last week, when she got back from **Atlantic City,** she had this **DOPEY GRIN** on her face . . . like she'd had **plenty** of **SEX!**

You **friggin'** idiot! **YOU** were with her in Atlantic City!! **YOU** were on your **HONEYMOON!**

And I **NEVER TOUCHED her!!** I **TOLD** you she was foolin' aroun'!!

Okay, you dirty two-timing broad!! Where **WERE** you?! Who were you **MESSIN' AROUN'** with?!? "HOT LIPS" HOROWITZ? "LOVER BOY" LUNDIGAN?!? "ROMEO" RICOTTA?!

F'r cryin' out loud!! I jus' took out the **GARBAGE!!** I was gone a minute and a half!

You **gotta stop** wearin' yourself **out** like this, Jerk! Listen . . . you got a big **return match** with Sugar Ray comin' up! You gotta **concentrate** on that! You **promise** me you're gonna **concentrate** on **nothin'** but the Sugar Ray fight?

Okay . . . I promise . . .

Way to **go,** Jerk!!

He's in **terrific form!**

I never **SEEN** him so sharp!!

SOK! BAM WAK

Now, **you** do **that** to **SUGAR RAY,** and you're a **shoo-in!!**

You **friggin' tramp!** Take **that** n' that! **THIS** will teach you to cheat on **ME!**

I AIN'T cheatin' on you, you **damn** fool!!

Yes you are! C'mon! Tell me **WHO** you been cheatin' **with,** or I'll **KILL** ya . . . !

Okay, you **really wanna know?!** I'll **tell** you! I been cheatin' with **Clark Gable, John Wayne, Haile Selassie, Pres. Truman,** and your **own brother, Shmoey!**

My God! A friggin' **ORGY!!**

POW!

You **idiot!!** Can't you see she's **JOKING?!?** I ain't cheatin' on you! Don't you think I got any **family loyalty!** I would **NEVER** cheat on my **Brother . . . !!**

That's **RIGHT!** I'm **married** to him, and **I know** Shmoey better than **ANYBODY!** He would **NEVER** cheat on his **Brother!** On his **WIFE,** maybe, but **never** his **Brother!**

Boy, that LaMutha sure made a **MESS** out of his life!

Yeah! His own Brother **walked out** on him, his Wife **hardly talks** to him, and now, **Sugar Ray** is poundin' the **crap** out of him!

And look at the **SHAPE** he's in! You **can't tell ME** he's a **Middleweight!**

No?!? Take another look at his **middle!**

The Race To The Crossing

Scenes We'd Like to See

ARTIST: GEORGE WOODBRIDGE WRITER: GARY BELKIN

I'm **Gene Sizzle** and this is my plump partner, **Roger E. Bear!** We're helping MAD Magazine do **something** they've **never done** before — **review** a movie while it's **still playing** in the theaters instead of doing it **so late** that **no one** remembers the film **they're spoofing!**

Right! This film asks some **unsettling questions** without giving any **enlightening answers** — such as, why do the Martians **attack Earth** in the first place? So join me and my **balding cohort** as we screen **MAD's version** of...

Why is it that **scientists** never **detected life** on **Mars** before?

It seems that **Martians** live underground!

Uh-oh! **Creatures** who do **that** a lot tend to be **mean, angry** and **vicious!**

I know! We **already have** that kind of **creature** right here on **Earth!** They're called **New York City Subway Riders!**

Nicholson also plays a **Las Vegas** promoter...

My **new hotel** will be a **complete replica** of **Los Angeles!** Every **half hour** we'll have either an earthquake, mud slide, forest fire, celebrity multiple homicide or a riot! And all our employees will have written unsold screenplays and our managers will be part-time agents and full-time phonies!

Oh, wow! You're bringing **reality** to an **entirely new level!**

As a recovering alcoholic, I wish you wouldn't drink in front of me!

Hey, **YOU'VE** got the **drinking problem** not me!

MARRED ATTACK!

ARTIST: ANGELO TORRES   WRITER: STAN HART

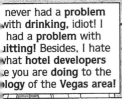

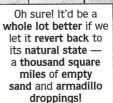

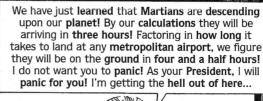

There's a **guy** who **owes** me **money** and I want you to **lean on** him for me!

I don't do that **anymore!** Since I **joined Louis Farrakhan** and **The Nation of Islam**, I've **reformed!** I now know it's **wrong** to **hurt people** ...unless they're Jews!

When they **come out** of their **spaceships**, we'll be prepared to **hit** 'em with **everything we got!**

That would be a **terrible mistake!** They may have come **in peace!** A **full-scale battle** would be **disastrous!**

Just to be **safe**, why don't we follow **"The President Bush Strategy"** used in Desert Storm — **deploy** our **forces, surround them** and then, when they're on the **brink of surrender, stop** the **war** and **declare ourselves** the **winner** without ever damaging their **military potential!**

We want you to **know something** about us! We will concentrate on **bringing peace** between our **two planets...**

HOORAY!!
YAY!!

...**Another thing** you should know is that **we have** a very **short attention span!**

Why are they **taking her** into their **spaceship?**

Maybe they **saw her** making **broadcast history** on TV!

Do you think they'll **do anything** to **her?**

I know **I would!**

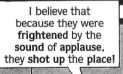

Marlon Brando was **busy** tonight so I thought I'd ask **famed astronomer** and **publicity junkie Carl Sagan** to tell us **what's going on!**

I believe that because they were **frightened** by the **sound** of **applause**, they **shot up** the place!

Applause, eh? If that's the case, we have **nothing to worry** about when THIS **movie** is over!

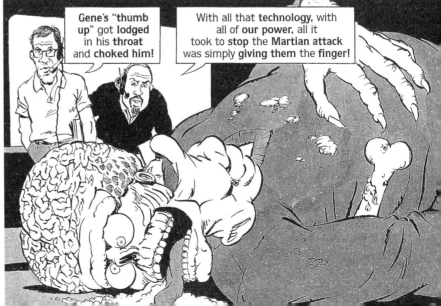

When we recently saw the trailer for a certain Jodie Foster/Matthew McConaughey film we were psyched: it looked to be the best outer space flick in a long time! But alas there were no gory aliens, no cool light saber battles, no thrilling jumps to hyperspace, no high-speed inter-galactic chases and no teeth-rattling laser blasts! It was just a bunch of preachy, pseudo-intellectual, faux-religious Carl Sagan redux tripe! They could have made a bad-assed action flick, but instead they took the...

I'm Dr. **Ellie Outaways**, astronomer! I've always been **fascinated** by the **outer galaxies**! When I was a **kid**, I spent **endless hours calling** into **outer space**, trying to make **contact**! But the **only contact** I ever made was with my **angry neighbors**, who told me to **stop using** a **megaphone** and **start using** a **radio transmitter**! I had a very **supportive father**! He bought me my **first telescope**! I used it to **scan** the **stars** in the **heavens**! He used it to **scan** the **motels** on the **hill**! He said we were **both looking** for **heavenly bodies**!

I'm **Palmer Loss**, ad-visor to the **President** on **religion**! I tell him **how far** he can **stretch** the **truth** without it being a real **bad sin**! **I'm a busy man**! I be-lieve **God made man**, and **my mission** is to **make women** — like Ellie! And I **believe** I can **do it**! **Real belief** can **make miracles**!

I'm **David Humdrum**, the President's **science advisor**! I keep the President **up-to-date** on the **latest scientific mat-ters**! Right now I'm supposed to **prepare** a **report** on **future space ventures** between the **United States** and **Russia**, but you can bet **nothing's** going to happen in **that area** until the **Cold War** finally ends and the **Berlin Wall comes down** — but that could take **forever**!

Greetings! I'm **Rachel Constant-Pain**! It's my job to **protect** the **President** by keeping the **press** at a **distance**! I've always been able to **do that** with a **smile** and a **few kind words**! Of course, this **adminis-tration** is **so corrupt** I have to keep the **press** at a **distance** with an **Uzi** and a **few hand grenades**!

PICKET FENCES (GET IT?)

OFFICIAL-LOOKING PAPERS

AM FM BEM

my first any

BAH-BOOMP-BAH-BOOMP-BAH-BOOMP

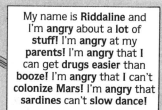

Hello, I'm **Charlton Heston.** I once starred in a **sci-fi flick** about an **astronaut** who **returns to Earth** to find it ruled by **hostile apes!** Now, **33 years later,** director **Tim Burton** has inexplicably decided to try to **improve** upon this **classic movie.** It's a **good thing** you can't carry a **concealed weapon** in **California** because I think if **I** had a **gun** with me after watching this **travesty** I would have **blown my brains out!** Anyway, welcome to…

I'm Air Force Pilot **Neo Everyson!** I stole a **space pod** from the **Overdone Research Mother Ship** so I could rescue my **pet monkey, Periscope,** after they sent him out to do **complex space experiments!** When will they learn they should never send a **monkey** to do a **man's job!** Specifically, they shouldn't have cast a **lightweight actor** like **me** to do a **leading man's job!** I took off in the **22nd Century,** entered an **electromagnetic time warp,** and landed in the **26th century,** all in a **few minutes!** That means I was going over **a century a minute!** But don't worry! From here to the end of the movie, you'll be **amazed** at how things are gonna **SLOW** down!

I'm **General Raid!** Prime Mate of the Primates! A **chimp** with a **chip** on my **shoulder!** I'm all for the **total extinction** of all **minorities** and the taking over of **all the land!** Get the picture? In this film I "**ape Hitler**"!

I'm **Attack,** General Raid's most **trusted warrior** and **Head Grunt!** I'm more than happy to **slap the humans** around! It gives me a **chance to give back** some of the **abuse** I suffered in **The Green Mile!**

I'm **Lumbar,** Orangutan **slave trader!** You might think that **buying** and **selling people,** and even **children,** is **immoral!** Well, in certain **uptight** circles it might be! But when you make the slave dealer **cute, witty** and full of **corny puns,** it elevates **slave trading** to a **respectable** occupation — at least that's what the **producers** would like **you** to **believe!**

PLANET OF THE REMAKES
JANET JACKSON?
I'm Airy, the Senator's daughter! I may be a Simian, but I lobby for humans so that people on this planet won't be hunted and sold into slavery! And now that I've seen that hunk Captain Everyson, I'll soon be lobbying for interspecies "monkeying around"! Hoo baby! I haven't been so turned on since I saw that porno flick, King Kong!
I'm Senator Sandar, Airy's father, and I'm so torn! On the one paw, my daughter wants equal rights for humans! On the other paw, General Raid wants them all dead! I don't know what to do! I wish this was America! Then I could just decide the way most of their politicians do — make laws depending upon the highest bidder!
I'm Caribou, full time human, part-time washed-up rock singer! I took this part because it was custom made for me! I've lived such a hard real life, I didn't need any make-up at all for this movie! I just showed up on the set looking like this, and I fit right in!
I'm Dame, the sexy blonde love interest! Well, the human love interest, anyway! I was put in this movie for one reason: to look numbingly perplexed and bewildered for two hours! I give the audience watching this movie someone to relate to!

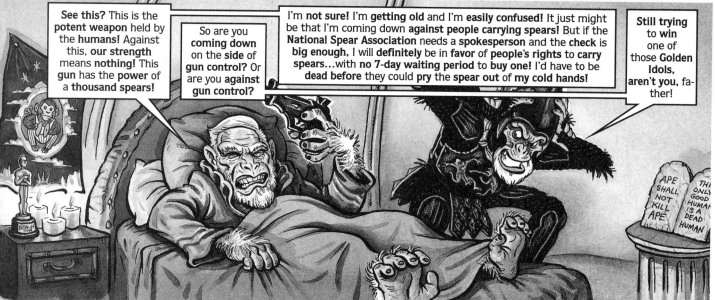

OF THE WORLDS

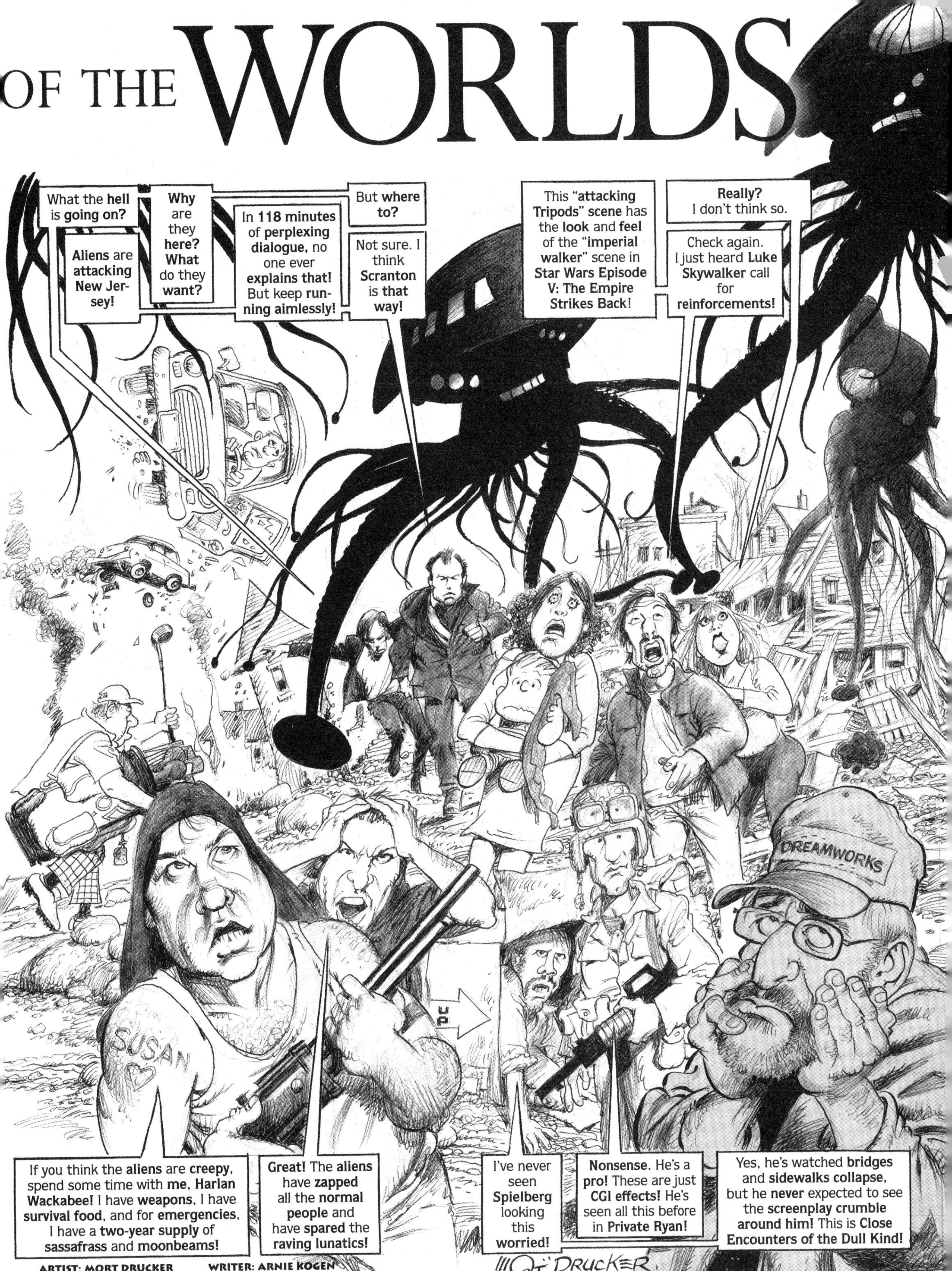

ARTIST: MORT DRUCKER WRITER: ARNIE KOGEN

First there was the trillion-selling book, then there was the illustrated version of the trillion-selling book. Then all the books about the book. Then the controversy about the book. Then the books about the controversy about the book. Then the commercials for the movie based on the book. By the time this hunk of crap actually made it to theaters, we were already in…

THE DaVin

I'm **Roving Languish**, a **professor** of **symbology** — the study of the interpretation of **symbols** and **codes**. It's not an **exact science** and, as you will see, when practiced by **yours truly**, it's not even an **interesting** science! Despite my **years** of **study**, I have **no idea** what the precise **mutilations** across this man's **chest** mean. Likewise, I haven't a **clue** why he's **naked** and laying in this particular spot in the **Louvre**. But my **doctorate** in Symbology does tell me **one important thing**. Based on the **symbolic nature** of the **chalk line** around his **body** drawn by the **police**, I can say with reasonable **certainty** that **this man** is **dead** as a **Dodo!**

I'm **Sofa**. I'm a **cryptologist**, and if you think this **plot** is har[d] follow, wail till you try to **understand** what **I'm** saying with [my] heavy **French accent!** I have much in common with **Rovin[g]** Languish. We both **decipher** things. We're both **wooden.** We're both **monotonous.** We're both — well, you'll soon lea[rn] just how **expressionless** we can be! I came to the **Louvre** t[o] give **Roving Languish** a **note** telling him that he's a **murde[r]** suspect! The note **also** warns him "not to **react** to this news[."] What was I **thinking?** Like he could **react** to **anything!**

I am **Bozo Farce**, a **French detective**. I'm here to **solve** a **murder**. **Nothing** escapes my **keen eye**. I ranked **high** in my **French detective class** — right behind **Inspector Clouseau!** Roving Languish thinks I brought him here to offer his **cockamamie explanation** of this man's **death**. The **truth** is, I think **Languish** killed the **curator!** Proof? Languish is an **American** — that's **all** the **proof** a **French detective** needs!

I'm **Bishop Angry-Rosa**. I'm a member of the **Opie Daze**, a group dedicated to keeping a faith-shattering **secret** about a certain **young lady** who was seen with a certain **bigwig religious leader** at a certain big **"last dinner"** party. To tell the **truth**, I can't see what the **Church** is so worried about. The **bigwig** was seen with a young **lady**, not a young **guy!** These **days**, that's a **positive** story for the **church!**

I'm **Styleless**, an **albino monk** who ser[ves] as the **Bishop's assassin**. I travel ever[y]where **killing people**. The **Bishop** sai[d] it's what **God** wants. It must be on a pa[ge] in the **Bible** I missed! Excuse me no[w] while I go **beat myself**. You may wond[er] why I'm into **self-flagellation**. Hey, yo[u're] sitting here reading this **ridiculous sati[re]**, I might ask **you** the same question!

KELLY

WRITER: DICK DEBARTOLO   ARTIST: MORT DRUCKER

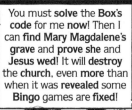

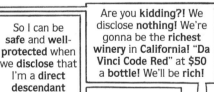

Here's a film everyone is getting behind. Um, no. Change that. This is one of the most touching films you'll ever see. Uh, no, scratch that. No. Don't scratch anything! This is a film chicks dig, but a lot of guys are afraid to get into. Aw, shucks, one last try... Take a lazy summer, add majestic scenery, throw in two hunky ranch hands and a thousand sheep – and nothing good is going to come out of this situation. Except box office gold! Here is...

BARE MOUN

My name is **Emmis Dull Mar**. I'm a man of **few words**. Most of them **mumbled** and **inaudible**! I'm on the **quiet side**. Keep things to **myself**. A **stranger** to **emotional expression**. Okay, I have the **personality** of a **wood chip**! This film is about the **summer of 1963**. Something happened to me on **Barebutt Mountain** that **changed** my **life**. And, it **wasn't poison ivy!** I don't **regret** what happened for **one minute**. Heck, if it **didn't** happen, there is **no way** movie audiences would **sit** for **two hours** watching a coupla dudes **herd sheep** and **eat beans!**

I'm **Jock Twitt**. I'm a hard-riding **rodeo cowboy**. But in this film, **saddle sores** are the **least** of my **problems!** At Barebutt that summer I discovered a **new activity** and it was a lot **more fun** than playing the **harmonica!** Society frowned on what **Emmis** and I did. It was **dangerous**, it was **painful!** We **snuggled** in the **sagebrush**, we **tumbled** in the **tumbleweed** and unfortunately, one time, we **cuddled** in the **cactus!**

I'm **Jolt Agoura**, the **ranch owner!** Somethin' **strange** and **unnatural** is going on up there in **Barebutt** between them two **cowboys** I done hired. But **I** don't mind. I figure if they have **each other** then they'll leave my **sheep alone!**

ROCKING "B"-HIND RANCH

DON'T SHOOT! I'M A REPUBLICAN!

SHHHHH! BE VEWY VERY QWIET! I'M HUNTING LAWYERS!

I WISH I KNEW HOW TO QUIT EWE!

I'm **Philip Seymour Hoffman**. This year I played **Truman Capote**, so I know a few things about the **gay lifestyle** in **1963** and believe me, it was **not** accepted in **America!** How **things** have **changed!** In **2006** the **gay lifestyle** gets you **nominated** by the **Academy Awards!** Besides **this** film, **Capote** and **Transamerica** got recognized. I bet the **Walk The Line** producers are **killing themselves** that they didn't include the song "A Boy Named Sue"!

I'm Vice President **Dick Cheney!** I was **proud** to be from **Wyoming**. But I **gave up** my **residence** when this film, excuse the expression, "**came out**." I'm looking to find a **place** in **America** that has **no gays at all!** I think I **found** one. A **phone booth** in **Jasper**, Indiana!

BUTT ITAIN

We're **Alamo** and **Latreen**. We're the **wives** of the **gay caballeros!**

We've got the **worst** of all possible worlds. We've got two **gay husbands** hangin' around the **house** all day — and they're **not redecorating it!**

We're **great-looking**, we're **hot**, we're **bitchin!** What a **waste!!**

Talk about **frustrated**. That's **us!** We're the **original** Desperate Housewives!

I'm **Ang Lee!** I **directed** film. This is a **sensitive, powerful, touching** film. Unfortunately, some movie-goers are calling it **Crouching Cowboy, Hidden Cattle Prod!**

I'm the ghost of **John Wayne**. What the **hell** has **happened** to the good old-fashioned **Western?** We've gone from **True Grit** to **True Fruitcake!** What **next?** **Nathan Lane** and **Ryan Seacrest** in a **remake** of **Stage Coach!?** I'm **turning over** in my **grave!**

I need a couple of **hands** to tend **sheep** in **Wyoming!** What's your **experience?**

I can **ride**. I can **rope**.

I can **mumble**. Specialize in long, unexplained pauses!

Okay. You're **both hired!** The **pay** is **forty-three cents** an **hour**, no **dental plan**, no **dancing with wolves!**

I **think** we can **live** with **that** — sort of!

How's the **grub?**

The **baked owl** was good and the **porcupine loaf** was okay. Didn't much care for the **coyote pudding!**

Tomorrow night... **bear claws!**

You mean those little **sweet cakes** called **bear claws?**

No, I mean real **bear claws!**

Yummy! I **love** those!

WRITER: ARNIE KOGEN   ARTIST: TOM RICHMOND

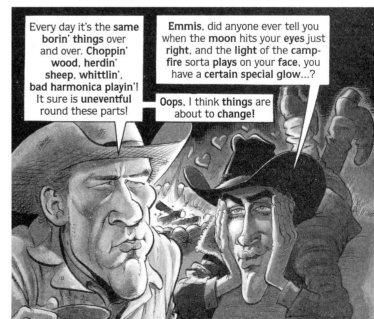

Every day it's the **same borin' things** over and over. **Choppin' wood, herdin' sheep, whittlin', bad harmonica playin'!** It sure is **uneventful** round these parts!

Emmis, did anyone ever tell you when the **moon** hits your **eyes** just **right**, and the **light** of the **campfire** sorta **plays** on your **face**, you have a **certain special glow...?**

Oops, I think **things** are about to **change!**

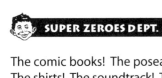

The comic books! The poseable action figures! The trading cards! The graphic novels! The TV special! The shirts! The soundtrack! The videogame! And.... um.... oh yeah, there's a movie somewhere amid all the merchandising! With all those greedy tie-ins, is it any wonder these geeky freaks are called the...

My name is **Professor $**, and I **created** the **$-Men!** I recruited **five bizarre freaks** and **drilled** them like **soldiers** until they could perform **together** as a **single unit!** I **got** the **idea** from the **guy** who started **The Backstreet Boys** and **'N SYNC!**

I'm the **$-Man** called **Cyclod!** I first **knew** I was **different** when I was a **child!** I tried to **read** a **bedtime story,** and I **burned** my **house down!** You might **think** it's **cool** to have **nuclear-powered eye-balls,** but there's a **down-side!** My **weekly Visine bills** are **through the roof!**

They call me **Deform!** I have **supreme power** over the **weather!** I know I'm an **awful actress,** but it could be **worse!** It could have been **Al Roker inside** this **suit!** Although **I'll** admit that **Willard Scott** has a **much** more **natural** looking **wig** than **mine!** When I **auditioned** for this **role,** I had to **act** like I was **creating** a **killer hurricane!** Afterwards, the casting director paid me a **huge** compliment! He said, **"Wow, you really blew!"**

Vasoline's my **monicker,** bub! **Life** is a **highway,** and I've got **road rage!** My **foot,** your **ass...let's do lunch!** As you can see, I have a **crucial role** in **$-Men!** I'm the **only one** who can deliver **dumb catch phrases!**

I'm **Rogaine,** a super-hero with the **ability** to **suck** the **life** out of **anything!** You know, **just like George Clooney** and **Joel Schumacher** did to the **Batman franchise!**

I'm **Jean Greypoupon,** and I'm so **dull** that I don't **even** get to **have** a **super nickname!** I possess the **ability** to **read** other people's **minds!** I can foretell **exactly** what a person **will do next!** That's **not** so **amazing,** though...with the **lousy predictable script** they **gave** us, **anybody** watching **this movie** can do the **same thing!**

Here at the **Academy**, we have a state-of-the-art medical center, a **private superjet** and **hangar**, and an **underground series** of **titanium-tubed hallways**! It's the **only** way **mutants** can have a **refuge** from the **enemies** in our **government**!

Shrewd, baldy! Instead of wasting **200 gajillion dollars** on all that **crap**, why don't you spend **half** as much **money** making campaign contributions to **Congress**? It's **much cheaper** to **buy off** politicians so they'll **vote** the **way** you **tell them**, compared with **building** your own **super-brainwave room**!

You're very **lucky!** It just so **happens** that **we** have a **vacancy** for a "dangerously unpredictable psycho slasher"!

Well gee, thanks, but **no thanks!**

What about your **past?** Those **experiments** in your **youth?** All the **drug-induced flashbacks?** I can **help** you **discover** what happened **25 years ago!**

Have you ever helped anybody else with a problem like **mine?**

Of course I have! George W. Bush!

I **ooze liquid** in **5 seconds!** Pretty **impressive**, huh?

Not **really!** When you **wiggled** on screen, **half** of the **dateless losers** in the **audience** had something similar happen! **Many** of them in **LESS** than 5 seconds!

Yow! That is the second biggest bug zapper I've **ever** seen!

Yes, but it still **needs...** more power! Slobber-goof... Load...you **know** what... to do...

Clap on! Clap off! Clap on, clap off!

They **turned** me into a **mutant!** Then, I **survived** a **1,000 foot drop** onto **jagged rocks!** Then, I **swam** across the **ocean!** Then, I **magically** knew the **right way** to **walk** all the **way** from the **beach** to your **school** in suburban **New York** without **anyone noticing!**

The **sad** thing is that the Senator's **explanation** of how he got **here still** makes **more sense** than **how** Al Gore **got** to his **Social Security plan!**

Since the birth of their **existence**, they have been regarded with **fear, suspicion** and **hatred**. Are **mutants** the **next link** in the **evolutionary chain**, or simply a **new species** of **humanity**, fighting for their **share** of the **world**? Either way, **one fact** has been proven. **True mutants** will line up outside **cineplexes** for **hours** and **hours** and jack any **moronic comic book movie** up to **#1** its **first weekend**! Hey, and **why not?** It's not like they're **wasting** their **disposable income** on **dates** with **girls!**

$

We're **smart**, we're **brave**, and we can **solve** the **world's problems!** No wonder **everyone** in **Washington, DC** wants us **dead!** Give us **half** a **week** and they'd **all** be **out of jobs!**

Despite my **great power**, I feel very **inadequate, Professor $!** I'm **Jean Greypoupon**, the **only $-Man** without a snappy **super-nickname!** How embarrassing! I'm a **psychic empath**, which means I can **pick up** anyone's **thoughts** or **read** their **emotions**. Which means I totally **kick ass** in **"Go Fish"!**

I'm **Icepack**, and when somebody's as **cold** as **me**, their **nipples** are **stiff 24/7!** Add the **rubber suit** and it's **NOT** a **pretty picture!** The **flamer** is **Piehole**. He's my **roommate** at Professor $'s **Academy for Hormone-Addled Mutants.** Our **arguments** over where to set the **thermostat** are unreal!

Icepack's **freezing ability** is exactly **equal** to **my powers** of **hot**. Fire vs. ice! It's a **brilliant dramatic device** that puts the concept of **"what is a hero?"** into **stark relief**, which the... ah, **who am I kidding?** We just **stole** the **Heat Miser** and **Cold Miser** bit from **The Year Without a Santa Claus!**

Rogaine My m**utant** power **enable** me to totally **suck, s** There h**as** been a**guy** like me **in** the Ova**l Office** since **1**

I'm **Cyclod**, and my **head** contains some sort of **bottomless energy source** that can **slice** through **steel** and **concrete** like Jell-O! But somehow it doesn't **kill me**, or even give me a **headache**. And they say there are no **believable heroes** anymore! Because I'm so **powerful** and also want to **look mysterious**, I constantly wear these **dark goggles** — just like **Tom Cruise**, Howard Stern, or **any number** of other **show biz jerks!**

Make way for **Vasoline**, bub! I'm an **adamantium-injected**, unstoppable **death machine** who **kills** with a **smile!** That's why I'm a **hero** to every **comic book geek** who's afraid to **squoosh** the **spider** in his **garage!** And yet, I'm **haunted** by my **past!** Huge gaps in **memory**, drug-induced **flashbacks** and **berserk violence!** I wish they did **Behind the Music** specials for **superheroes**, so I could find out **where I've been!**

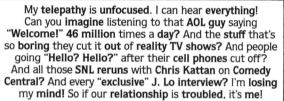

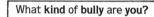

I like **you** too, Icepack. But it's **dangerous** for y'all to make **physical contact** with **me**!

Hey, **I'm 200 degrees below zero!** Put your **tongue** anyplace on **me**, and it's like getting it **stuck** to the **flagpole**!

"**X**"-this, "**X**"-that! "**X**," "**X**," "**X**"! And yet there's not a smidgen of **sex** anyplace in **this** movie! We **should** be **called** the **PG-Men**!

Gasp! Being **squeezed**... to **death**! **Gurk!** **Never** should've **taken**...that **Flintstone** chewable vitamin...with **iron**!

My **son**...a **mutant**? I should have **suspected**! When I was **nursing** you as a **baby**, you used to give me **double frostbite**!

His **family's** having **trouble accepting** him. Are the **filmmakers** using **mutants** as a **metaphor** for **discrimination** against **gays**?

Get **dressed** for the **next number**, and I'll **answer** your **question**...in SONNNNG!

Are you **crazy**? How can we **land** a gigantic **jet plane** like **this** on a **residential street**?

It's **registered** to Professor **$**! He's got **handicapped plates**!

I cain't **believe** that **Vaseline** jus' got **shot** by a group o' **trigger-happy cops**! He's **white**!

Look at that **gaping hole**! It's **almost** as **big** as the **one** in the **plot**! Why would the **President** order General **Strykethree** not to use **excessive violence** against **mutants**, and then tell the **Air Force** to **shoot down** a **jet plane** the **next day**?

Ignore that, and **look** on the **bright side**! America's **back** to considering **explosions** on **airplanes** to be "**good, old-fashioned summer entertainment**"!

We'll set up **camp** here. I just **hope** we can keep **warm overnight**!

Here, we might as well use these **Oscars** for **kindling**. After **appearing** in these moronic **X-movies**, who even **remembers** when we used to do **quality work**?

I knew from your **scent** that you **weren't** the REAL Jean Grey-poupon!

That's what I get for **eating eight chili dogs**! But I **can** become **anyone** you **wish** me to be. Let me **change** into **someone** more **comfortable**. Would you prefer to see me as **Deform**? Or **Rogaine**?

How about you turning into Professor $ for **15 minutes**? But let's go **slow**! When I leave **scratch** marks down your **back**, they're **permanent**!

Surprise! Although after disguising myself as a **janitor**, Senator Smelly, a barroom **bimbo**, Jean Greypoupon, **Rogaine**, **Deform** and **Vaseline** in the movie so far, maybe "**surprise**" isn't **exactly** the **right word**!

You'd **better** disguise yourself as Roger Ebert next! That is, **if** you ever want to get a **positive review** for this repetitive CGI clip reel!

I'm a **little girl**. And I'm **afraid**. But I'm definitely **NOT** a diabolical **psychic illusion** projected by your **enemy's mutant son**! Can you **help** me, **sir**?

Naturally, dear! My **brain power** is **limitless**! I can **manipulate minds**! I can **transform matter** itself!

Oh **yeah**? Then how come you don't **fix** your **legs**, so you can **get** out of that **wheelchair**?

Hmm... frankly, I **never thought** of that!

So **much** for your "**limit-less brain power**"!

With my **psionic powers**, I could **control** Scott's **personality**. If only he **had** one! It's as if **Scott's** being **forced** to **attack** me **against his will**!

I **am**! The **videogame company** that has the **$-Men license** has **already** designed a **level** where we **fight**! So this **movie** has to **stick** in a **scene** to match!

I have **claws**!

I have **claws**!

I have **speed**!

I have **speed**!

I get up to **3 mil** a picture!

Okay, I'll **die** now!

Gaaahhh!! I've only felt **one other kind** of **pain** this **intense**! Whenever my **hus-band John Stamos** makes me **sit down** with him and **watch Full House reruns**!

The **super-duper brain ray** is **killing** every **mutant** in the **entire world**, **except**, for some reason, **Magnesia**! How can **Magnesia** manage to **survive** against some-thing this **powerful**?

Sequel power! If this **dumb ray** actually **worked**, you can kiss **$-Men 3** goodbye!

Ha! **Last time**, I strapped a **mutant** into some ridiculous **super raygun** and tried to **zap** all the **humans**! **This time**, I'm going to use the **raygun Prof $** is strapped into to **zap** all the **humans**! I can't tell you what my **ingenious plan** will be for **$-Men 3**, though. It's a **big secret**!

INCREDIBLE OPPOSITE SWITCH!

Yaaaa!!!! My **brain**! It's **breaking apart**!

The **ma-chine** is **killing him**!

It's **not that**! Somebody **flicked** the **wrong switch** and I'm getting **Lite-FM** in here!

"I can be **your hero**, baby. I can **kiss away** the **pain**."

DESIGNED FOR Microshaft **Windoze** ⊗P

My **eyes**! For **no special reason**, I'm **blind** now! Oh well, **at least** that **makes me luckier** than the **audience**!

Wow, a blind **Marvel Comics superhero** in a **movie**! There **hasn't** been one of **those** in almost **three months**!

And it gets **worse**! **Magnesia** just **convinced** his **shape-shifting scaly woman** to **trick** the **evil General's** deformed **mutant son** into **reversing** the **brainwave machine** so that it **siphons** the **power** of the **mind-controlled good guy** who thinks he's **helping** the **invisible girl** and **zaps every human** on the **planet**!

Haw! Take **THAT**, Merchant-Ivory!

If you **let me live**, I'll keep **dropping** more **tantalizing clues** about your **lab rat past**!

No sale! My **"confused search" schtick** is the **only** thing **separating** me from the **other $-Men**. Take **that** away and **soon** I'll be **just another** one of the **schlub characters** who have to say things like, "What **is it, Professor**?"

Wow, the **bad guy's compound** gets **totally destroyed** at the **end**! What a **shocking twist** — if this were **1963**! Apparently, this flick has the **mutant ability** to **absorb** the **ending** of every **James Bond movie ever**!

Mr. President, after **destroying** a **U.S. military base**, we created a **dangerous thunderstorm**, snuck into the **White House** during **heightened security** and **erased** your **staff's memory** for **just one reason**: to let **you** know **we** can be **trusted**!

Good enough for me! Let me **chuck** this **"Axis of Mutants" speech** I was **going** to **read** to the **nation** and I'll just **free associate**!

A **guy** with **nuclear eyeballs**, **no problem**! The guy with **foot-long metal blades** that **boink** out of his **hands**, totally **believable**! A **President** capable of **expressing** an **original thought** without a **poll-tested script**? No way!

 **SITH HAPPENS DEPT.**

Turmoil has engulfed the movie industry as legions desperately await the next Star Bores epic. Hoping to resolve the matter, greedy director George Lucas begins filming while dispatching his lawyers to sign merchandising deals throughout the galaxy. As the geeks endlessly debate who's cooler, Darth Maul or Boba Fett, moviegoers everywhere waste hours waiting on line, only to discover that after all the hype, this story-free, poorly-acted flick's nothing more than...

I'm **QuiteGone Jim**, Jet-Eye Master! I am **closely attuned** to the **living Force**, but I follow a **different path** than most Jet-Eyes! I made sure I got **killed off** in the **FIRST** of these **three lame flicks!**

I'm the **young Oldie Von Moldie!** I've **nearly completed** all my **training** as a **Jet-Eye apprentice!** As a matter of fact, I'm so **close** to **graduating,** I've already had my **picture taken** for the **yearbook!** I was voted "**Most Likely to Succeed** in **Sequels**"! As part of my **Jet-Eye training,** I built this **light saber** with my **own** hands! It can **cut through anything**... except the **overblown special effects** to this **overdone story!**

I'm **Death Hideous** from the **Dark Side!** I inspire an **unsettling sense** of **dread,** like those "You have **performed an illegal action**" blurbs that suddenly **spring up** on our **super-sophisticated computer screens** when you haven't done a thing! My **lifelong dream** is to put an **end** to all **peace-loving Jet-Eye Knights!** I spread **evil** via **holographic transmissions** from my **headquarters** on **Croissant** — and to *really* annoy folks, I send 'em **COLLECT!**

MAY HIS LOSS BE WITH YOU!

ANTIQUE JUNK

MASTEL

MOTHERS AGAINST POD DRIVERS

I'm **Mannequin Skystalker**, apprentice to **Jet-Eye Master QuiteGone Jim!** Even at my **young age,** I can feel the **Force within me!** Either that, or it's **puberty kicking** in a little **early!** I'm also in **training** to be a **loyal** and **obedient Jet-Eye!** Already I learned how to **roll over, beg,** and **fetch** a light saber! To be a **Jet-Eye,** I had to **abandon my mother** so that in the **future,** I can become the **father** of **Lube Skystalker** and **Princess Laidup!** Pretty **confusing,** considering that **everybody knows** how this **cash-milking saga ends!**

I'm **Shamu,** Mannequin Sky-stalker's **mother!** I know this **sounds strange,** but Mannequin **doesn't have** a **father!** I guess you could call it an **immaculate MIS-conception!** Oh, okay, so I **did** have a **husband,** but he made me **promise** I'd **never tell anyone** who **fathered** such a **rotten little actor!**

I'm **Queen AmaDilly,** leader of the No BooBoo Nation! When I was **younger,** I wanted to be either a **fashion model** or the **ruler** of a **small nation!** This is the **perfect combination** — I rule a **small, starving nation** AND I'm **emaciated** and wear lots of **weird clothes!** My **vow** is to keep NoBooBoo a **peace-loving place,** no matter how many **battles** and **blood baths** it takes to do it!

STAR BORES
EPIC LOAD I
THE FANDUMB MEGAMESS

I'm **Creepio**, a **droid** on the planet of **Tattoo!** Believe it or not, I was made from a **huge mess** of **wires** by nine-year-old **Mannequin Skystalker!** In effect, he was my **father!** My **mother** was a **plate** of **spaghetti!**

I'm **Death Mall**, and I wield a **double-bladed light saber!** It's not quite as good as that **triple-bladed Gillette Mach 3**, but I can give my opponents a **damn close shave** anyway! I revel in the **evil** of the **Dark Side!** My scary **tattooed face, glowing evil eyes** and **horned skull** mean only one thing: **KISS** just might be able to **stage a comeback** after all! Don't **believe me?** See **page 43!**

I'm **Har Har Blinks**, a Gungun! **Gunguns** are **extremely intelligent** beings, which is kinda **hard to believe** since we all tawlk wike **liddle baybees** wid **iwrating voices**, like **Baabaa Walters** on **speed!** Truswt mee, a **liddle Gungun** goes a **roooong waay!!**

I am **Lace Windows**, the only **black** **senior member** of the **Jet-Eye Council!** Actually, that **isn't bad**, when you consider that the **other members** are mostly **green, yellow** and **magenta!** As a **senior** member I no longer wield my **blue-bladed light saber** and I **don't get to say** a heck of **a lot!** But I do **enjoy** a **10%** senior citizen's **discount** at the **Jet-Eye commissary** and gift shop!

I'm **Bar Stool!** I was a sort of **glorified garbage can** in *Star Bores IV, V, and VI!* But now it's **years earlier**, so I'm an **earlier version!** I'm just like the **later model**, only **without** the **driver's side airbag** and **automatic pencil sharpener!**

Yodel I am, a **senior** member of the **Jet-Eye council!** **Famous** I am for over **800 years** of **dispensing wisdom!** I was the one who **proclaimed:** "The **Dark Side** is hard to see in a **dim light**"! And "Why do they call it a **light saber** when it **weighs ten pounds?**" Find these **wise**, you **do not?** Well, **800 years old I am!** Gems they all **cannot be!**

I'm **Pikachu!** Although I'm **not in this movie**, I'm here to **learn** from a **master!** No, not a **Jet-Eye master!** I'm talking about **George Lucas** — a **merchandising master!**

I'm **Mannequin Skystalker!** I made my **own droid,** and my **own pod racer!**

Droids he makes! **Pods** he makes! Does he ever make his **own bed?!** You should see his **room!** It's a **mess!**

Let me **guess,** you **must be his mother!**

Wow! There's that **Jet-Eye intuition** kicking in **again!**

I made a **deal!** If **Mannequin wins** the **pod race,** we get the parts to **fix** our **ship,** and he **goes with us!**

If he **loses?**

He's **STILL free** to go with us! He's so sickeningly **cute** the people here would **PAY** to **get him off** this **planet!**

I **don't care** what they say, I **like Mannequin** just the way **he is!**

Har Har! How come your **speech** is suddenly perfect?

Cool it, **I'm the Queen!** That's **Har Har** in my **dress!**

Watching me **race** my pod is pretty **exciting,** unless you happened to see *Return of the Jedi,* which had a **much more exciting** race through the **giant redwoods** on flying scooters!

If you see the guy **selling frankfurters,** send him **over!** I'm **starving!**

You want to **eat frankfuters, Chubby the Fatt?**

No, the guy **selling them!** He looked **delicious!**

Mannequin won the race, so he's free to leave the **planet,** but we can't **take you with us!**

Can I go **study** with the **Jet-Eyes?**

Yes! And then **study even harder** to **learn how** to **act!**

I'll **keep my eye** on him too! I've developed more **maternal instincts** toward him in a **week** than his **cold-hearted** mother has in his **whole lifetime!**

We come before the **Jet-Eye Council** to tell you that the **SissyLords** are back and making **trouble** for the **Republic!**

The **Sissy-Lords?** They've been **extinct** for years!

Extinct, no! Maybe in the **closet** for a **millennium,** but now they're **out** and **they're pissed!**

For the **Republic** trouble **making** are **SissyLords!**

I just **figured it out!** Yodel isn't wise, he's just **verbally dyslexic!**

45

J.K. Rowling wrote a book that changed the way kids read.
By the second, Barnes and Noble faced a huge stampede.
Hollywood took notice, as their eyes lit up with greed.
"Grab the rights," screamed agents, "There's no way this won't succeed!"
At last, the movie's in the can, and fans can't wait to peek,
So they can jump online and post a withering critique.
For every detail overlooked, they'll howl and curse and shriek.
Well, we don't care. We got it wrong. Now shut your pie-holes, geeks!

I'm **Harry Plodder, boy wizard**, and my story is **unique!** You'll see me **slowly discover** the **ability** that I always had **hidden inside!** Just like the young characters in **Toy Story, Terminator, The Sixth Sense, The Matrix, The Lion King, Ghost** and every single **Star Wars!** What makes **my** character **unique?** I have an **owl!**

I'm the most **powerful wizard** in the **world!** As soon as I picked the weekend to **open our movie,** look at how **fast** I made every other **chickenspit movie company** in Hollywood disappear! Poof!

I'm **Runt Queasy,** wannabe **wizard** and fulltime **whiner!** Usually, the "**sidekick**" gets all the **funny lines,** but the **hero** gets the **girl!** But in **this** movie, there **aren't** any **funny lines,** and **nobody** gets **anybody!** Why do you think I spend **so much time** up in my **dorm room** dressing my **pet rat** in **sexy outfits?**

Herwhiny Grungy here! Me and **Runt** add a little "**masculine-feminine**" **dynamic!** Except **I** bring the **masculine,** and **he's** in charge of **feminine!** All three of us are making our **film debuts!** The **producers** entrusted their blockbuster to **newcomers** because we have a **youthful freshness,** we don't come with "**past role**" baggage...and they don't have to **pay us squat!**

HALFWIT EXPRESS

I, **Severely Snapped,** am here to provide a **classically British tone** with my **withering sarcasm!** Unfortunately, when it comes to **wit,** my **comedic idols** are the **Spice Girls!**

I am **Druckermort — pure evil!** I killed Plodder's **parents** but **failed** to kill the **boy!** To **protect** him, **Doubledork** inexplicably sent **Harry** to live for **12 years** with the **Doodlys —** a family of powerless **buggles** who don't care if he **lives** or **dies!** Is it just me or is Doubledork's wizard hat on **too tight?**

Professor Qwerty here! Even though Prof. **Snapped** acts **scary** and **evil,** the **bad guy** is secretly **ME, ME, ME!** This should come as a shocking **surprise twist** to anyone who **didn't read** the **first book...or in other words, all **three** of you out there!

Plodder

AND THE SORRY~ASS STORY

ARTIST: MORT DRUCKER   WRITER: DESMOND DEVLIN

My name's **Drano Malformed**, and if you've read the **book series**, you know that I am an **obnoxious child** of **privilege**! But despite my **superior connections** and **wealthy background**, somehow **Harry** keeps **beating** me! **That's** why they file the books under "**Fiction**"!

My name is **Albus Doubledork**, and I run the **Halfwits School** for **promising wizards**! Our school is comprised of four houses! **Griddlecake, Flavorflav, Ramensoup** and **Slipnslide**! We provide our students **guidance** on living in a world of **buggles**! In **wizardspeak**, a **buggle** is a helpless person with **no power** whatsoever. Kind of like a **liberal** trying to speak on the **Fox News Network**!

I am **Professor McConjugal**, Deputy Head-mistress and Creepy Dame! We on the **faculty** provide constant **encouragement** to the children so that, if they **work hard** and **apply** themselves, they too can become **weird old coots** like us! **No wonder** the school's **dropout rate** is **94%**! I hope these **first years** stay, though! We need to film the next **six sequels FAST**, before these three **kid actors** grow up into non-cute **ex-kid actors**! A **23-year-old Harry Plodder** is **NOT** going to be **pretty**!

Booooo, I'm **Nearly-Headless Schmuck**! I think it's **weird** for a guy to walk around with his **head** hanging **sideways?** Just take a look around this **theater!** Half the **audience** is already in the same position, **sleeping!** Some of these **poor parents** are here for the **15th time!**

I'm head galoot **Rubiks Haggard**, an' I handle all o' Doubledork's **secret missions!** After all, what could be more **inconspicuous** than sendin' a **400-pound biker** wi'h an **accent** that makes **Antonio Banderas** sound like **books on tape?** They play **dirty** in **Hollywood**, though! **Lucas Films** is already **suing** me, for impersonatin' a **Wookiee**!

Rrrr! Woof! We're in charge of **guarding** the **secret chamber** that holds the **Cirrhosis Stone!** You know what they say... **three heads** are **better** than **one!** Especially when you're **licking yourself!**

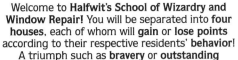

Welcome to **Halfwit's School of Wizardry and Window Repair!** You will be separated into **four houses**, each of whom will **gain** or **lose** points according to their respective residents' **behavior!** A triumph such as **bravery** or **outstanding achievement** will get between **5** and **25 points**, but **rule-breaking** will cost your house an amount up to but not greater than a **triumph** of **equal magnitude**...

...unless the action is committed by **two** or more **students** from **opposing** houses, in which case, **professors** from the **unaffected houses** will be given a **secret** amount of **points**, which will be **divided** between the alternate students based on **seniority** and/or **culpability**, including the **inactive period** between **terms**!

What does the winning house get?

No one **knows!** Nobody's **EVER** been able to **figure out** this cockamamie **points system!**

I am the amazing, **I** go on **top** of each **head,** **And I pick** the **house** for **every student,** **While I** sing my **dumb poem,** **Which** sounds **horrible,** **And doesn't rhyme,** But come on, it's **not bad** for a **damn hat!**

Every **first-year** has to put on the **Snorting Hat!** That way, **all students** start their **education** with something in **common!**

Yeah! **Head lice!**

Your studies... shall begin... at **DAWN!**

Did you ever **notice** that the people in this **movie** try to **juice up** really **boring** dialogue with **dramatic pauses** and **emphases?**

For **breakfast...** I shall be eating... **MUFFINS!**

But **tonight...** let us watch... **BECKER!**

'Arry, say **hello** t' yer very own **owl!** From **10 am to 11:30**, 'e helps you with yer **spells!** An' from **4 pm** to **5 pm**, 'e helps yeh **send letters!**

What happens from **11:30 to 4** in the afternoon?

Yeh'll be scraping **owl poop** off every **flat surface** in here! **Filthy beast!**

Excuse me, is this **Flying Class?**

I'm **sorry**, but I'm **unable** to answer that at this time! Your **regular instructor** was unavoidably **held over** with an **earlier** class! There will be a **brief delay** while the **9 am class** is rescheduled...for **3:30 tomorrow afternoon!**

This is **air travel** all right!

Haggard, Headmaster **Doubledork**, I have **much** to learn! Is there **anything** you two **CAN'T** do?

Yes. **Shave!**

I don't know about **you**, but **I'm scared!** Mostly because the way this movie's **grinding along**, the plot's actually being **livened up** by a game of **Chess!**

I know how to **win!** You've got to let the **white queen** knock me **out!**

Runt, we can't!

Do it! It's the **only way** to defeat Druckermort! And **besides**, it'll be the **first** and probably **last time** I ever get **touched** by a **woman!**

Two of these **vessels** contain **safe elixirs!** **Two** contain **poison!** And **three** contain the deep-down **satisfying flavor** of **Diet Coke! Mm-mmm!** Just for the **thrill** of it, just for the **chill** of it, just for the **taste** of it, Diet Coke!

Is it **me**, or is "**product placement**" in movies getting **out of hand?**

Professor Qwerty! It's **you**, and the evil Druckermort! He's leeching off your **host body**, just like **Liz Smith!** But, how could there be a **face** on the **back** of a **person's head??**

If her **plastic surgeon** yanks **Joan Rivers'** skin up any **tighter**, we'll find out!

I've already got the **turban**, and now I've got an **extra face!** I could be the **perfect** New York City **cab driver!** But tell me, **Druckermort**, and be **honest!** From back there, does my **butt** look **big** to you?

For **bravery**, I award an extra **100 points** to **Harry Plodder!** For **cunning**, **another 100** to **Harry Plodder!** And because his **name** is the freakin' **TITLE** of this movie, **3,000 more points** to **Harry Plodder!** Harry Plodder's house **wins!**

Hey! How can **Doubledork** just **make up** brand new **totals** after the winner has **already** been **decided?**

Easy! He used to be on the **Board of Elections** in **Palm Beach, Florida!**

All's well that ends well, **Harry!** You're **alive!** And the **Cirrhosis Stone** has been **destroyed!**

Destroyed the Stone? Thanks, **genius!** If you were going to **destroy** the thing all along, couldn't you have destroyed it on **Page Three?** You know, **BEFORE** Qwerty and Druckermort kicked my butt into the **hospital? Oy!** Something tells me the **next six Harry Plodder** movies are all gonna be **downhill** from **here!**

It was a time of ill tidings. Good men fell, and great woe and calamity shrouded the realm. And nowhere was the scourge more bleak, or the disaster more vast, than in the land of New Line Cinema! Many disasters at the box office nearly put them in the land of perpetual darkness. Just as there seemed to be no future for New Line or its bottom line, a single shaft of hope pierced the gloom. Nay, not one shaft of light, but THREE! A trilogy of movies sure to entice every fantasy-hungry role player, isolated mouth-breather and embittered loser in the land to make the arduous trek to the cineplex again, and again, and still again! Hopefully the fortunes of New Line would be restored, but only if a wary public did not become…

Why did they **choose me** to play **Dodo Gaggings?** Obviously, it **wasn't** for my **talent** as an **actor!** The **director needed** to find the **right person** to portray a **Slobbit** who is **3 feet, 6 inches** tall! After they put **2-inch lifts** in my **shoes,** we were in **business!** You've **never** seen a **lead character** like **me!** I may be the **first action-adventure hero** in **movie history** who could get his **ass kicked** by Harry Potter!

On the **other hand,** I made my **reputation** as **one** of the **finest Shakespearean actors** and have been **nominated** for an **Academy Award! As Gandoof,** I **wear** a **fake beard** and **silly hat** and **play** the **part** of a **great magician** rather **convincingly!** Watch closely as my **credibility** as an actor **totally disappears** before your **eyes!**

I'm **Peppercorn,** but some call me **Spider! Others** call me Longstinks, the Renuzit, Elfdro or **Telemundo!** I've got more stupid **extra names** than P. Did and the **Wu-Tang Clan combine** What I **don't** have is a **decent** shampoo and **conditioner!**

As **Spam Gangrene,** I'm **chief tagalong nebbish** and **sidekick!** I'm **dim-witted, afraid** to **talk** to **girls** and an **all-around nothing —** in **other** words, I'm **this** film's **target audience!** If I **wasn't** in this **movie,** I'd be **first** on **line** to see it!

We're **Pimple** and **Baggybuns,** the two most **incompetent Slob-bits** around! Give either of us **half** a **chance,** and we'll **stick** our **foot** in our **mouths!**

Which **ain't easy** when you're a size **78 Wide!**

I'm **Billboard Gaggings, oldest** living **Slobbit!** On the **outside,** I **appear** to be a **friendly, happy-go-lucky fellow!** But **everybody** can **see** that just **beneath** the **cheery surface,** I'm **really** a **twisted, bitter, jealous,** desperately **unhappy** dwarf! Just like **Billy Crystal!**

As **Argon,** the **immorta** Elf princess, people ask me, was it **hard** findi the **inspiration** to play bizarre ancient charact who goes on **forever?** Actually, it came easy t me! My dad is **Steven Ty** from **Aerosmith!**

RED OF THE RINGS

EEBLE SCHTICK of KA-CHING!

am **Borderline**, and I am **valiant**, strong and **brave**! I have **pledged** my life against **evil**, in **hopes** that I can **return** to my **homeland**, which **has** been completely burned and **destroyed**! I said I was **valiant**, **strong** and **brave**... I **never** said I was **smart**!

As you can **see** from my **bow**, I am the **archer Legolamb**! My **archery skills** are **unsurpassed**! My **acting skills**? Let's **put** it **this way**, I'm so **off target** I've **hit** the **screen** of the next **cineplex**! Tom Cruise's **butt** in **Vanilla Sky**, to be **exact**!

Behold **Aspercreme**, the bad guy **wizard** with a serious **wand up** his **butt**! **Gandoof** never **realized** that I was on the **side** of **evil**! He **should** have **gotten** a **clue** when I **pulled** a **rabbit** out of my **hat** and immediately **put it** into a **blender**! I hate **Gandoof** for his naive **faith** in **goodness**, and also because his **facial hair** is **two inches longer** than mine! **Size does count**, even in the **wizard world**!

I may **look** like something that got **coughed up** by a **400-pound cat**, but I'm **Gimmicki**, the **angry dwarf**! How do **I** figure in **all** this **confusion**? I'm **waiting** for **someone** to tell me! I'm **not sure** if I **appear** in this **segment** or **either** of the **next two** they filmed!

You're **lucky**! I **know** I **appear** in this **episode**, but as **one** of the **Dorcs**, the allegedly **deadly creatures** in **service** of Sorehead's **evil desires**, we have a **higher mortality rate** than **sitcoms** on the **WB**!

As **Galapagos**, the all-knowing **elf queen**, I'm the **wisest character of all**! And to **stand out** even more, **notice** how I'm **backlit**! Like someone in a **feminine hygiene commercial**!

Eh! Eh! Me am **Golfclub**, and **me** have been **driven insane**! **Not** by **Ring**, by this **cockamamie three-hour butt-blistering movie**! Look at this **splash page**! Talk about **endless**! And it only **includes** the **main characters**! Characters? It was **easier** to keep the **dogs straight** in **101 Dalmatians**!

I'm **sorry** we took the **main road** and **got you** caught!

And that we tried to float the raft away, leaving **you** to **get killed!**

And how in the **bar**, we told **everybody** who you **really** were!

Not to mention the **campfire** that we set **attracted** the **horsemen**, and **you almost died!**

That's **okay.** But would you mind **not** leaning on my **bad shoulder?**

See? I **told** you **this** little creep holds grudges!

You'd **give up** your **immortality** to **marry** me? **What** made you decide?

We're about **90 minutes** into an **eight-hour trilogy**, and already it **feels** like a **lifetime!** Suddenly "forever" doesn't **seem** like such a **great thing!**

We've got to **band together** to **stop Sore-head!**

Sorehead is getting **more powerful** by the **minute!**

Soon, **Sorehead** will **strike!**

Uh...does it strike **anyone** as strange that the **#1 bad guy** in this movie isn't actually **IN** this movie?

Dodo, I want you to have **this.** It's **magic Slobbit chain mail** that will **protect** you from **harm!**

Nice timing! The only way this gift could **matter more** to me is if I'd gotten it back in the Shire! You know, like **BEFORE** I got stabbed?

By **hiking** across this **mountain**, we'll **sneak** into Torpor **unobserved!**

Yeah, who could **EVER** spot **nine black silhouettes** doing two miles an hour against 400 miles of **pure white snow**? Shrewd!

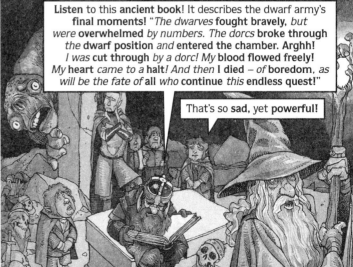

Listen to this **ancient book**! It describes the dwarf army's **final moments!** "*The dwarves* **fought bravely**, *but were* **overwhelmed** *by numbers. The dorcs broke through the dwarf position and entered the chamber. Arghh! I was* **cut through** *by a dorc! My blood flowed freely! My* **heart** *came to a halt! And then* **I died** *– of boredom, as will be the fate of* **all** *who* **continue** *this endless quest!*"

That's so **sad**, yet **powerful!**

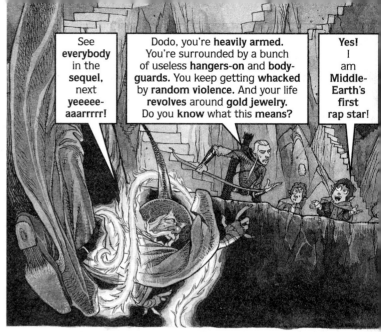

In this **one room** we **have** more than **20** known **species** of **rare spiders**, at least **18** different **species** of **rodents**, and it's **also home** to **one** of the **largest insect larvae** collections in the **world!** But **now** it's **time** to **leave** the **school cafeteria** and **go** on our **field trip** to the **Genetic Research Institute Of Creepy, Crawling Things!**

This is the **jumping spider, genus Michaelous Jordanous!** And this is the **crab spider, genus Itchy Skineous!** Here at the **lab,** we have **begun** what was once thought **impossible: inter-species genetic transmutation!** But **that** of course, is **preceded** by **inter-species dating, dining** and **dancing!**

What would **happen** if **one** of those **spiders** bit **you?**

It would be **impossible** for one of **those spiders** to **bite you!** There's four feet of **solid glass** between **us** and the **spiders!**

Well **I just got bit!**

Damn! We're on the **wrong side** of the **glass!** Oops, **sorry** about **that!**

This is **weird!** Since I was **bitten** by that **spider,** my **hands** are becoming **filled** with **tiny hairs!** Am I **finally growing** a **beard?**...No **signs** of that! Just my **hands!** Is it **possible** that the **rumor** about... **Nah!**...I'm **spooked!** I think I **need** a **snack!** Maybe a **few juicy flies** and a **stagnant pool** of **putrid water!**

That was **amazing!** You **caught** me, and **my tray!**

I'd **hate** to see you **lose out** on **eating** your **lunch!**

Actually, I **don't think** I'm **going** to **eat it!** You **kept** my **tray** from **hitting** the **floor,** but **now** for **some reason,** there are **long strands** of **gooey stuff** all **over** my **food!** I haven't **eaten** yet, but **I'm** about to **lose** my **lunch!**

I guess **Peeper likes me!** When you got **fresh** with me, he **gave you** some **powerful punch!**

So he **knocked** me **into** a **locker!** Big deal!

That **locker** used to be **three floors down!**

Oh, **like** it **takes** some **kind** of **special force** to **knock** someone through **three ceilings** and **up** against a **locker?** It was **just** a **lucky punch!**

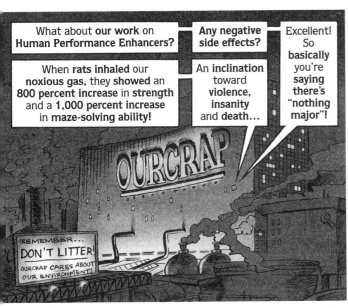

THE FAKING OF THE PRESIDENT DEPT.

When a movie comes out in the spring and gets a ton of critical acclaim it usually means one thing: if it came out in the fall along with all the other movies looking to cop an Oscar, nobody would even notice it at all. Unfortunately, the producers of this film have bigger problems at hand. Praised though it may be, once the big summer movies like Jurassic Park and Last Action Hero come out, this film is sure to take a box-office...

DIVE

ARTIST: ANGELO TORRES　　WRITER: ARNIE KOGEN

That was **quite a nice thing you did today!**

Forget it! Sorry about Cheyenne!

You're **not** the **real** President, are you?

No, I'm **not!**

Then let's meet officially! I'm Helen Twitchell!

I run a **temporary employment agency!** I'm Dive Kowlick!

For a **great guy** you've got a really **goofy name!**

Yeah, it **ranks up there** with "Sigourney"!

Vice President Nunce! So nice to meet you after **three fourths** of the film!

It **has been a strange experience!**

What, that you, **Walter Nunce**, a Vice President have been **shunted off** to India?

No, that I, **Ben Kingsley**, an **Academy Award winning** actor has **less film time** than **Jay Leno!**

Yes, I **was** involved in the **S&L scandal!** I think you're **entitled** to **honesty** from your **President!** You're also **entitled** to **good jobs, clean air, cable repairmen** showing up on time and **films** where a **common man** makes **stirring speeches** restoring **simple virtues** and **down home values!** In other words, you're **entitled** to a **Frank Capra film!**

Well, that's my **last speech!** My **work** here is **done!**

And you've **thawed** the **First Lady's heart!** I love **Frank Capra** films **too!** I'm coming **with you!**

I **too** have been **moved** by your **innocence** and **charm!**

Tell me, would you **really** give **your life** for **the President?**

That's **my job,** Mr. Kowlick!

Would you **take a bullet** for me?

Not **me personally!** They've **hired** an **agent** who looks **just like me** to do **that!**

Well, I'm **back** where I belong —running a **temp agency!**

And **I'm going to be here with you!**

So it **all ends happily ever after!** I love you, you love me, the President's still a **vegetable!**

But **who's running** the country?

This **movie** has shown that any **dumb schnook** can run the **country!** I've placed another "**average Joe**" in the **White House** who has those **qualifications!**

Let's see... carry the ought... subtract the **six...!**

THE BUTTAFUOCO STOPS HERE

There is unrest in the movie theaters. Several thousand multiplexes, under the leadership of George Lucas, are foisting more stiff acting, droid-like dialogue and convoluted plotlines upon a weary and disgusted public. This unfortunate development has made it difficult for the extremely limited number of remaining fans to maintain interest in...

STAR BORES

I'm **Oldie Von Moldie, Jet-eye master!** There is **great unrest** in the **Galactic Senate!** So **what else** is **new? Hell,** the **day** the **unrest stops,** this **endless parade** of **mind-numbing Star Bores adventures** will **end** and my **confusing life** will **finally** be **over!** I mean, I **started out** as an **old man, then** I **died, then** I was **young again!** Now I'm **aging** all over **again!** No one **ever knows** how many **candles** to **put on** my **birthday cake!** The only **good news** is that I'm **young again,** but because of a **book-keeping error** I **still** collect my **Senior Jet-eye pension!**

I'm **Mannequin Skystalker, apprentice** to **Oldie Von Moldie!** I was an **apprentice** in the **last Star Bores** movie, and I'm **still** an **apprentice!** Jet-eye **knights** may have **hi-tech equipment,** but what we **really need** is a **strong union** to **fight** for **quicker advancement!** Then again, it **might** be my **rebellious attitude!** Jet-eye law **forbids romantic attachments,** but **Senator AmaDilly** and I have been **practicing docking maneuvers!** I'm **not worried,** though! **Now** that she's a **politician,** if anyone asks, AmaDilly automatically says, "I **did not have sex** with that **Jet-eye, Mr. Skystalker**"!

I'm **Senator PetMe AmaDilly,** the **former Queen** of **No-boo-boo** and **current Skystalker heartthrob!** I've **joined** the **Galactic Senate** to **vote** on the **critical issue** of **creating** an **Army** of the **Republic** to **assist** the **overwhelmed Jet-eye knights!** I'm **also pushing** a **vote** for **women** to get some **easier-to-take-care-of hairstyles!** These **ridiculous do's** take **hours** a **day** to **wash, set** and **blow-dry!**

Meesa is **Har Har Blinks!** It'sa **amazin' howsa** many **peoples hates meesa! Wella MADsa** gonna do **youse** a favor **George Lucasa nevers** do! **Thisa** is **only time** yousa see **meesa! Yousa** can say **thanksa** to MAD **bysa** subscribing at **madmag.com!** Tell them **Har Har sentsa yousa!**

Master Yodel am I! Dispensing **wise sayings** have been **doing I forever!** "May the Force Be With You" from my **mind** has **come!** Okay, so **originally** I said maybe: "With you, may the force be," but **basically still** my **idea** it **is!** I **talk** always **asteroid backwards!**

I'm **Bar Stool,** sometimes **known** as **R2D2!** I just **heard** some **bad news!** Now **there's** a **newer model Astromech Droid, R4D4,** which is **much more powerful** than me! **Hoo boy!** Now I know **how** the **Sega System felt** when the **XBox** came **along!**

I'm **Damn Weasel, bounty hunter!** My **mission** is to **kill Senator AmaDilly!** This **vial contains** poisonous **Kewpies!** I **plan** to have my **droid release** these **creepy, crawling things** in her **bed! Though,** to be **honest,** I think **AmaDilly** is **much more** worried about **another insect ruining** her and **everyone** else's **summer — Spider-Man!**

ARTIST: MORT DRUCKER   **WRITER: DICK DEBARTOLO**

I'm **Lace Windows**, senior member of the **High Council**! I'm **quite concerned** by the **growing disturbance** in the **Force**! I'm even **more concerned** that all I **ever** get to **do** in any of these **movies** is, well, **look concerned**! In the **last Star Bores** movie I just **looked plain old concerned**, but in **this** movie, it's a much **more demanding role**, so you'll **see** me look **deeply concerned**!

I'm **Chancellor Palpitation**, head of the **Senate**! I have to be **very careful** that **anything** I **say** or **do** doesn't **cause** an **all-out war** with the **Separatwits**! The **Separatwits** have the **ability** to produce **millions** of clones **ready** to do their **bidding** — sort of like **Scientologists**, but less scary!

I am **Count Cuckoo**, **leader** of the **Separatwits**! Even though I'm **getting on** in years and I **can't get** my **light saber** to **work** like I **used** to **without special effects** — mainly **Viagra** — I'm **still** a **sharp adversary** to be **contended** with! And as **soon** as I remember exactly **who** my **adversary** is, he better **watch out**! Now **where did** I **put** the keys to my **Solar Sailer**? And **where did** I **put** my **Solar Sailer**? And **do** I **need keys**?

Kid Twisto, Jet Master! I'm in **film not** because **Republic** needed **help**, but because **Hasbro** did! **They** needed **one** more **action figure** to **round out** their **Star Bores** toy line!

I'm **Tango Feet**, the **bounty hunter** chosen to be the **template** for the **Army of Clones** that will **battle** the **Federation**! Each **clone** will have **all my** traits: my **genius-like intelligence**, my **superhuman physical strength**, my **superior cunning** and **agility**, and **most** of all, my **sense of modesty**! Oh, there's **one other thing** all the clones **share** with **me**: absolutely **no acting ability whatsoever**!

Hey **George**! **Alf** here! Why don't I have a **part** in this **film**? You want a **weird looking alien**? I am a **weird looking alien**! You want **attitude**? I **reek attitude**! You want something that's **100% owned** and **merchandised** by **Lucas, Inc.**? Oh, **that's** why I'm **not in this film**! Ha!

I'm **George Lucas**, and **I'm sick** of the **critics saying** that my **Star Bores** movies are **lackluster** and **repetitive**! I'd **like** to **see anyone** of them **write** the **same** movie **nine times** and make it **appear fresh**!

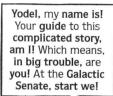

I finally caught you, **Damn Weasel!** Now **tell** me, who **hired** you?

It was a **bounty hunter** called **Ga-Ga-Gasp!**

Hmm... Ga-Ga-Gasp? That name doesn't **ring a bell!**

It's **not a name!** That **was** my dying breath, idiot! Ciao!

Now we're at a **dead end!**

To NoBooBoo, out of harm's way, Senator AmaDilly, Mannequin takes! Makes no sense, did that, to me, even!

Oldie Von Moldie is **too critical** of me! I'm **far** more **advanced** than he **thinks** I am!

Manny, don't try to **grow up** too fast! And please don't look at me like that! I can see what you're **thinking!**

Really? Come a little closer and you just might **feel** what **I'm thinking!**

The **power** of the **Force** is **with you,** that's for sure!

Meanwhile **Oldie, Trex,** he **does find!**

Can you tell me where this **poison dart** came **from?**

Can you cross my **palm** with **silver?**

No, but I **can cross** your **face** with my **fist!**

In **that case,** the **dart** is from the Planet **Kinko!** They're **cloners!** They **love** to **copy** things! They **make** clones 24/7!

"Here's the **forecast** for **Kinko!** Showers for the **next 2,000 Shanigans,** followed by **heavy rain,** followed by **thunderstorms!** The **weather** will **turn inclement** after **that!**"

We made **200,000 clone soldiers!** As soon as we **install** the **400,000 AA batteries,** they'll be **ready** for **battle!**

They're **cloned** from me, **Tango Feet!**

I **see** that! It **would** be nice if you had **stood up** a little **straighter** before they **cloned you!** Now we have **200,000 clones** with **extremely bad posture!**

Meanwhile, Mannequin on a **quest** for his **mother,** to **Spittooine,** he **does go!** Big help, **Whatzzup,** will be!

You think **finding** your **mother** will **really end** those **years of sleeplessness,** Manny?

I'm **positive** it **will!** She has a **prescription** to **help me sleep!**

Pills?

No, **she has** a **copy** of this **screenplay!** I'll **go right out!**

Let's **hope Oldie** isn't **furious** because you **disobeyed** his **orders** by **leaving NoBooBoo!**

We have **MegaMotorola Transponders** to **keep** in **touch** with **each other!** Of course, when I'm **this** far away, I **shut mine off** in **order** to **avoid** the **intergalactic roaming charges!**

Sometimes producers leave out a fact here and there when they make a biographical movie. But in a recent hit, Ron Howard left out a **ton** of facts here, there and everywhere! Facts like the subject of the movie was married several times, had a child out wedlock, liked to drink a lot and had numerous hetero- and homosexual affairs! Seemed like he was after anything in skirts **and** pants! Wouldn't it be more on the money to say this guy had...

A BOOTY-FULL MIND

ARTIST: ANGELO TORRES
WRITER: DICK DEBARTOLO

Your country needs you, Mash, that's **why** I **brought** you **here** to the **secret War Room** at the **Pentagon!** With your **incredible deductive powers,** we **want you** to help **crack enemy codes** for the **military!** It will be **your way** to **aid** our **country's fight** in the **Cold War!** And **if** you can **use** your **incredible deductive powers** to **help me** pick the **winning lottery numbers,** that will be **your way** to **aid** me **personally!** I'm **broke!** I only **own** this **one hat,** and as **you'll see,** I wear the **same suit all the time!**

With my **brilliant mind,** Pollack, I can **look** at these **rows** and **rows** of **numbers** and **immediately** make a **logical deduction!** Unfortunately, I'm not **so brilliant** since I **didn't ask** for a **percentage** of the **gross profits** of this **movie** instead of a **one-time paycheck!** Hey, can you **fault me?** Not even **my super brain** could have **figured** that this **totally fictionalized** and **homogenized account** of my **life** would **pull** in so much **hard cash!** However, I do see **another Academy Award** for my **acting!** I just **pray** I'm **not hallucinating!**

Plodder

AND THE LAMEST OF SEQUELS

ARTIST: TOM RICHMOND   WRITER: DESMOND DEVLIN

That **scowling curmudgeon** sticking pins in his Harry Plodder doll is **Prof. Severely Snapped!** He's an **embittered wannabe** who desperately wishes **HE** could be the **#1 man in charge**! But he'll **never** get the chance because **nobody likes him**. Think of him as the **wizard world's Al Gore!**

There in the corner is **Tom Riddler**, semi-invisible **bad guy**! He's really the evil **Druckermort**, but uses a **phony name**! He writes **misleading messages** back and forth with a young girl, **Ninny Queasy**, through an incredible **magic diary**. Why doesn't he just use **IMs** on **AOL**, like every other **perv** in the country?

Our newest teacher is **Corduroy Pockmark**, author of the **world's phoniest biography!** Every page is designed to **disguise** the fact that he's an **egomaniacal fraud**. He's the **Rudy Giuliani** of **wizardry!** He's written **dozens** of books, **all** with the **same problem:** he uses the letter **"I"** more than the other **25 letters** in the alphabet **combined!**

And the **star** of our little fiasco is **Harry Plodder!** He's got **incredible wizard powers** locked **deep inside**. He also has a lot of **personal pain** locked **deep inside**. In fact, **everything's inside** with this **blank-faced little stiff** – especially some **acting talent** which **he's yet to unlock!**

He's actually a **normal preteen kid** with **normal concerns**! Regular kids worry about **getting zits** and **blackheads**. Harry worries about the **glowing lightning bolt scar** on his **forehead** that he got the night his **parents got whacked**. Same basic concept!

But there **is something** that makes him **very different** from **everyone else**. And it's **not** his **mysterious past** or **unique talents**. It's that he's a **12-year-old** who actually **likes** being at **school**! What a **total wuss!**

Allow me to **explain** the Halfwits "**points system.**" Each of the four houses — **Griddlecake**, **Flavorflav**, **Ramensoup** and **Slipnslide** — **gains** or **loses** points as the semester goes on. It's a **great** way to **build school morale** — except for the **75% of our students** who get to end the year as **miserable losers!** Points can be **added** or **deducted** at will, **according to the plot!** And in the event of a **dispute**, the **final decision** goes to the **French ice skating judge** from the **last Olympics!**

I can't decide **which** classes to sign up for. **Potions lessons? Divination lessons? Flying lessons?**

Try **acting lessons!** You're no **Haley Joel Osment!**

Uh-oh! **Look out! Runt** just got a **Yowler!**

How dare you drive the flying car to school! You could have been killed! Or worse, we might have had to pay for the tree! I bought you some new underpants — extra snug! And they're camouflage to disguise any stains!

You're **supposed** to be the most **powerful young wizard** in the **world?** Why can't you **fix** your **eyesight** and **lose** the **dorky glasses?**

Oh, oh, oh YEAH?

Since I have **no way** of knowing **who started** this **argument,** I'm **forced** to deduct points **alphabetically! 10 points off Harry Plodder** and **Griddlecake** for **arguing!**

Huh? But "**Harry Plodder**" comes **after** "**Drano Malformed**"!

Still in a **fighting mood,** eh, Plodder? Make it **20 points off!**

Crappe! Goy! The **Chamber of Secretions** will be **opened this semester!** The **heir** of **Slipnslide** will **reveal** himself! We'll enjoy **10,000 years** of **unstoppable power!**

We **might** even get **bigger rooms!**

Crappe, you're a **classic example** of what happens when a school hands out too many **athletic scholarships!**

Don't worry about **gifts**, children! What do you **get** for the man who already has **everything,** not counting the **cervical vertebrae necessary** to support the weight of a human head? Come in! Have **fun!** After we're done playing **Pin the Tail on the Undead Donkey,** you can join our game of **Musical Coffins!**

Weird! I've **never** been to an annual celebration of **death** before!

I have! My parents once took me to **Wrigley Field** to see the **Chicago Cubs on Opening Day!**

Drat! Students have been **turning to stone,** and now there are **two fresh victims** — **Nearly-Headless Schmuck** and **Professor McConjugal!**

I'm **not petrified,** jerk! **This** is my **normal expression!**

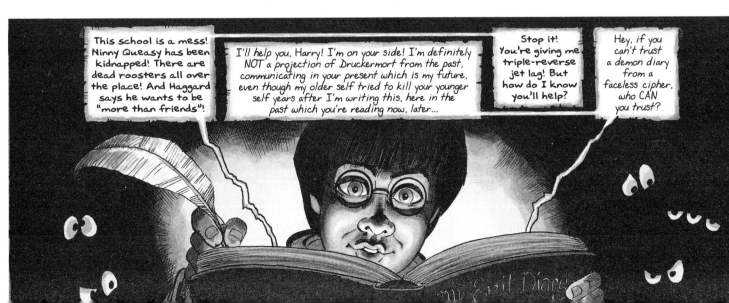

MAD FACTOIDS: Organizers of the 1996 Atlanta Olympics have voted to allow Carjacking, Tourist Murdering and Drive-by Shooting — but only as "demonstration sports."

BREAKING A NASTY HOBBIT DEPT.

How do you turn a dumb kiddie story into an "epic quest"? Make it big, make it long, and make it three times. Frantically cut back and forth between storylines, so nobody notices how drawn-out and repetitive each one is. Use made-up languages and subtitles to hide how boring the dialogue would be in English. Create a love story out of thin air. Every moment of alleged suspense should end with another character and his army showing up out of nowhere and saving the day. And whatever you do, make sure you buy the extra-large tub of popcorn. You'll need it before you're done! Because there are NO bathroom breaks during...

BORED OF THE RINGS

Unlike the **real movie, MAD won't** make you sit around **waiting** for **two** and a **half hours** before you get to see the **CGI** mayhem and the **computer-generated gore! Gaaaaaaahhhhhh!**

Fine, but **this** is **ridiculous!** They drew **all** the **characters together,** even though **half** of **them** aren't in this **battle scene!** They **shouldn't** be **allowed** to **screw around** with **true source material** like that!

It's **artistic license!** After all, the **filmmakers** made a **few changes** to the original *Lord of the Rings* **books, too!**

Books? These **ridiculous plotlines** come from **books?**

There are **many paths, Legolamb!** Some are **tangled** and **dark,** others **straight** and **true!** And they're all **crawling** with **unseen enemies!** But **enough** about my **hair! We're** the **good guys! We represent** everything that's **right** and **good** and **kind** in the world! So let's kill, kill, kill, kill, kill!

Gee, your **hair smells rancid!** No **wonder** you're the **king** of **long-distance relationships!** Me, I'm **here** to **supply** the **Fellowship** with a **softer side!** And it **sure** needs it! Over **10,000** **creatures galloping** through this **movie** and maybe **three girls!** There was **more** of a **feminine feel** to *Fight Club!*

Obviously you're **forgetting** my **incredible two-minute cameo scene!** It's **one** where I get **outacted** by a **dead guy! New Line Cinema** didn't **hire** me to play A[...] for my **emotional chops!** Get a **load** of the[...] **bad boys!** They're the **two towers** all tho[...] **role-playing virgins** out there in the dar[...] **theatre audience** wish they could **visit!**

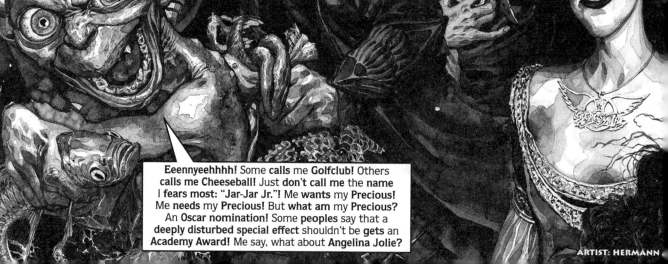

Eeennyeehhhh! Some **calls** me **Golfclub!** Others **calls** me **Cheeseball!** Just **don't** call me the **name** I **fears** most: **"Jar-Jar Jr."!** Me **wants** my **Precious!** Me **needs** my **Precious!** But **what am** my **Precious?** An **Oscar** nomination! Some **peoples** say that a deeply disturbed **special effect** shouldn't be **gets** an Academy Award! **Me** say, what about **Angelina Jolie?**

ARTIST: HERMANN

THE TWO + HOURS

I'm **still Dodo Gaggings,** and I'm **secretly carrying The Ring!** At least it was **supposed** to be a **secret!** Too bad **every** other **character** in the **entire trilogy** apparently knows **I'm hiding** it! My **number one dilemma** is that the **Ring's** evil **power** is **warping** my **mind!** It's **turning me** into a **quick-tempered, embittered, bug-eyed midget!** And **Spike Lee** says if I **steal** his **act,** he'll **sue me!**

Enjoy the **Spike Lee reference!** It's the **first** and **last time** in these movies that **you'll hear about** or **see** a **black person!** I'm **Spam Gangrene,** his **faithful sidekick!** But I've **got** my **own problems!** Can you **imagine** what it's like, **losing** a charisma contest to a guy with **one facial expression?** Confused shock, **confused shock, confused shock! Dodo** makes the **walking tree** look like a **method actor!**

There's **lots of wooden acting** around here, but **don't look** at us **trees!** You'll **never see** a bigger **pissed-off vegetable** than **me,** at least **until the next Vin Diesel film** comes out! **Angry, violent trees, walking around** and **kicking butt?** It's like the **ultimate horror movie for dogs!**

Gandoof here, complete with **flashy costume change!** Just call me the **VH1 Diva** of the **year 3019!** I've **gone** from **Gandoof the Gray** to **Gandoof the White!** Of course, I'm **not** as **young** as I **used** to **be!** Let's just say that my **wizard's Depends** are **off-white! Sorry, horsie!**

This **bloody battle** presents the **greatest fear** that any **warrior dwarf has!** My **last sight** on **Middle-earth** could be a **dorc's groin!**

Rrrrr! Do my **eyes deceive** me or is that **Gimmicki's twin?**

That's **no fat, hairy dwarf!** That's the **director, Peter Jackson!**

I'm **totally** into Middle-earth! In fact, my **middle looks** like **Earth!** While I **directed** these **three epics,** I **even learned** to **speak** in **Elvish, Sindarin,** and **Quenya!** The **only thing** I never **learned** to **say** in **any language** is **"cut"!**

WRITER: DESMOND DEVLIN

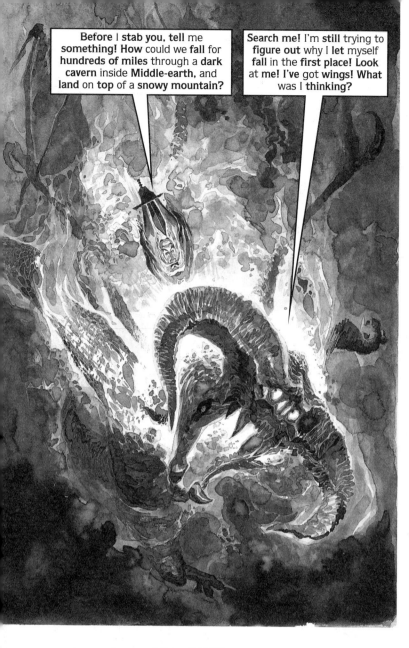

Amazing! I've never seen a living, talking tree! But **maybe** that's because I'm the **only person** on **Middle-earth** who's **never watched** *The Wizard of Oz*!

Watching you **herky-jerky trees** lurch and **lumber around** is like having **front-row seats** for a **Cavaliers-Raptors** game!

It's **true!** You **trees** are **very, very, slow!**

Slow, huh? That's **pretty big talk** for two "**heroes**" who spend **five hours** out of a **nine-hour trilogy** basically **hanging around, waiting for** to be **rescued!**

Come out, come out, wherever you **are!** Oh well, I've **searched** this area for **nine seconds!** What **more** can **I do?**

Hide, Master! It be a **Fazool!** **Thems only** have **one weakness! Thems** can **track** the **Ring** for a **thousand miles** right to the **exact spot** where **Master** is **hiding**, but **thems** can't **quite** find him **hiding under a tree!**

Astounding! It's Gandoof! We **thought** you were **dead!**

Yes, I guess it **would be** a **huge surprise** to **anyone** who **hasn't read** the **fifty-year-old books** and **didn't see** the **movie trailers** and **didn't notice** all the **publicity** featuring **Ian McKellen** and all **three** of you!

Before you **enter**, you must **surrender all** your **weapons!** But the **guy** with the **eight-foot oak staff shooting sparks** can **pass!**

D'oh! That's **what I get** for **hiring** special **U.N. weapons inspector Hans Blix!**

ARTIST: MORT DRUCKER   WRITER: ARNIE KOGEN

Fairest Shlump

That's my name! **Fairest Shlump!** Wanna **choc-o-late?** My **Momma** always said "**Life** is **like a** box of **choc-o-lates!** It's **got marsh-mallows** and **nuts!**" Some people say I'm like one of the **nuts**, but **others** stick up for **me** and say **my mind** is more like a **marshmallow!** And that I have a **bad southern accent**, like I'm from **Philadelphia!** What's so **bad** about **that?** It could **earn me** another **Oscar!** And that I **don't stop talking!** Like **now** for instance! **This** may be a **record** for the **longest dialogue balloon** in a **MAD satire!** But I do have **good posture!** The best in Alabama! One year I **won** the **State Posture Championship!** Maybe you saw the **newsreel** of President Roosevelt giving me the **trophy**, even though he **died** before I was **born!** Or **maybe** that was **Woody Allen** giving a **special effects trophy** to *Zelig!* I forget! Anyway, my **momma** always **said** that **posture** is like **oatmeal**...

That boy is **kinda** different!

That's like **saying** Arnold Schwarzenegger is **kinda husky!**

They **say** he has an **IQ of 75!**

In **some parts** of **Alabama**, that's **Mensa level!**

I'm very **concerned** about **Fairest Shlump!**

Why? He's **simple**, but **harmless!** He's a **lovable** innocent!

I guess I **worry** about **any man** who takes his **fashion lead** from Ed Grimley!

I feel like **telling** a perfect **stranger** the **story** of **my** life! Would **you** like to **hear it?**

Young man, you **are** a **complete** idiot!

Gee, that's **exactly** what they **said** when I was **born!** **That** was **way** back in 1945...

BUS STOP

CHOCOLATES

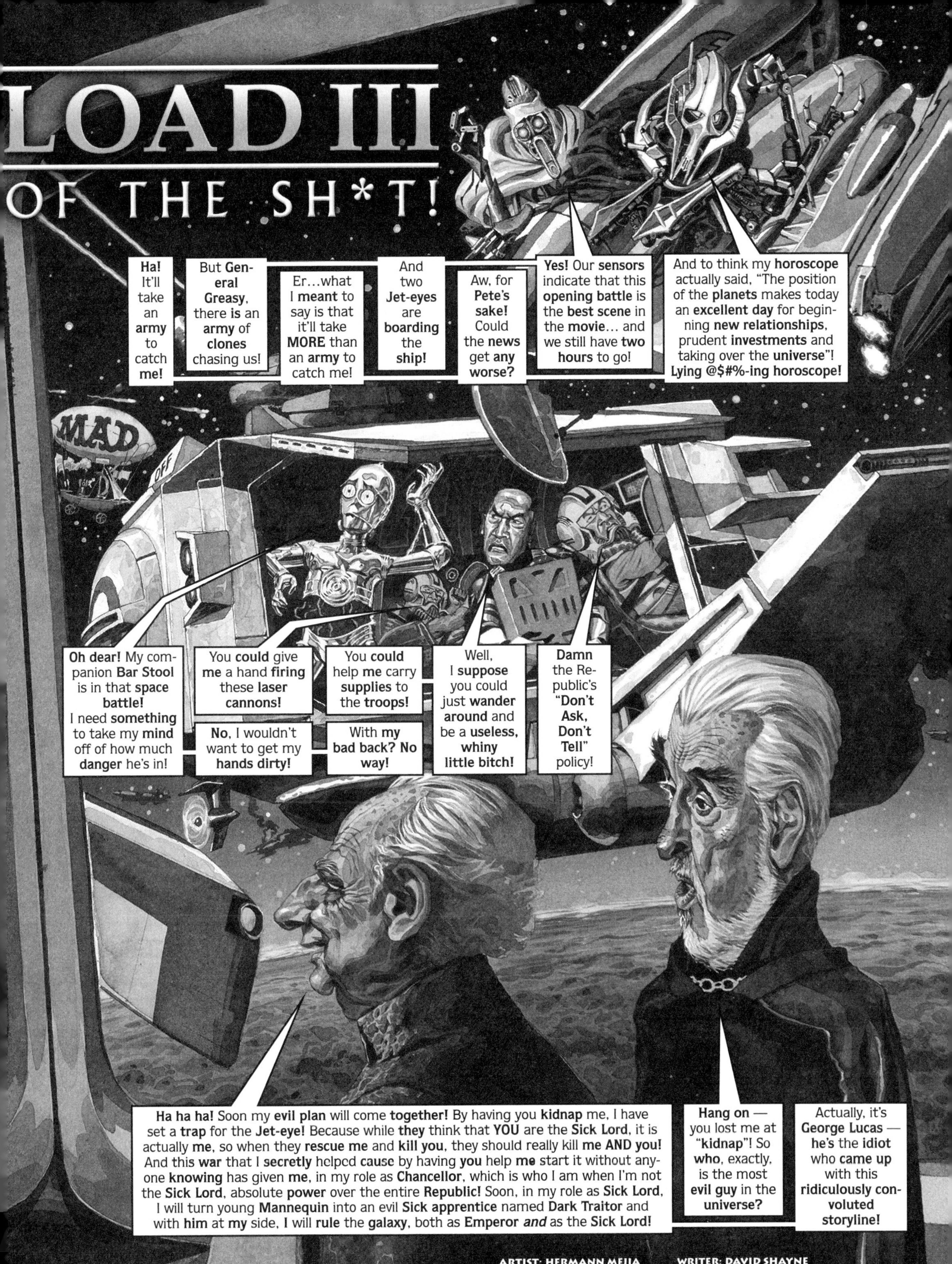

ARTIST: HERMANN MEJIA WRITER: DAVID SHAYNE

Mannequin, I am appointing **you** my **personal representative** to the Jet-eye Council! You will have **all** the **privileges** of a Jet-eye Master!

Awesome! I get a Jet-eye Master's **parking spot!** Access to the Jet-eye Master's **dining room!** A Jet-eye Master's **corner office** with a **view** of all those **cool ships** whizzing by! **Ten percent off** at the **Jet-eye company store!** What a **thrill!** What an **honor!** What a —

Mannequin, you're on the **Council!** You're **responsible** for reporting on all the chancellor's activities! But **one thing**, you're **NOT** granted the **rank** of **Master!**

Not a Master? ...but I still get the **ten percent off** at the **company store**, right?

Mannequin did not **take** to his assignment of **spying** on the **Chancellor** with much en**thusiasm!**

Much **anger** there is in **him!** Still **mad** about not receiving **rank** of **Jet-eye Master** he is!

How do you **know?**

An "I was **Appointed** to the **Jet-eye Council** and All I Got Was This Lousy T-shirt" **T-shirt** I saw him **wearing!**

And now to the **Woolie planet** I go so with the **Woolie army** the droids I shall **fight!**

Huh?

The **droids** I shall **fight** with **Woolies** by my side there will **be** on the **Woolie planet!**

I **still** don't **follow!**

To **war** I go, with the as**sistance** of the **Woolies**, who **fight** against the **droids** we **shall!**

After all these **years**, you'd think I'd be able to under**stand** you, but it **still** sounds all... you know, **backwards!**

Back**wards?!** Try to understand **this**, you should — me bite!

I think this **war** is de**stroying** the **principles** of the Re**public!**

Has it ever **occurred** to you that we might be fighting on the **wrong side** of this **war?** What if the **democracy** we were **serving** no longer **exists** and the **Republic** has become the very **evil** we have been **fighting** to **destroy?**

What are you **saying?**

That this **war** represents a **failure** to **listen!** And, since we **chew up** all this **time** making ponderous, long-winded **speeches** about **democracy** and **Republics**, it also represents a **failure** to make an "**action**" **movie** that actually has **ACTION!**

The **Dark Side** of the **Force** is a **pathway** to **things** that **some** consider to be **unnatural!**

Like **saving people** from **dying?**

No, like wringing every last **penny** out of a **franchise** with lame **licensing deals!** Speaking of which, wanna buy a **Darth Tater Mr. Potato Head?**

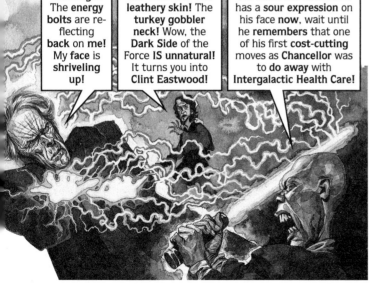

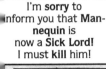

If you want to make a good, suspenseful movie, it seems rather obvious that you need a bold, clever idea and a smart, tightly-crafted script. But if all you have is a weak premise about a woman and her kid locked in some fortified area of their expensive Manhattan brownstone, then you have no compelling plot, no suspense, no on-the-edge of their seat audiences. What you have is the...

PANIC RUINED

This **townhouse features** a "Panic Room," a **super** fortified **hiding place!** **Notice** the high-tech **Sony security cameras** stationed **all over** the house, **connected** to a **bank** of **Sony TV monitors** and **Sony video tape machines loaded** with **Sony video tape!** It was **built** to **protect** the occupants from **undesirables**, namely **JVC, Panasonic, Sharp**, and the **other Sony competitors!** As a **Sony company production**, this **movie** elevates product placement to an **art form!**

This is the **perfect place** for **you** and **your** son...er, daughter...er, your **androgynous offspring!** There's **no other townhouse** like **this** in **all** of **New York City** — high ceilings, **hardwood floors** and the **possibility** of **discovering millions** of dollars rumored to have been **stashed away** somewhere by the previous **millionaire owner!** And it's in **great shape** considering his **greedy family** never **bothered** to **take** the **place apart** to **find** the **stash!** So **offer** the **sellers** their asking price, and **this place** can be **yours!**

Offer the **asking price**, just **like that?** You **never offer** the **asking price** on anything! I'm **spending** my **ex-husband's money** and I **want** to **make sure** I'm **depleting** it **fast** so his **new girlfriend** gets only the **worst part** of the **deal** — **him!** I say **double** the **asking price** and make **everyone happy** — except my $@#&* **ex!**

I **see** what you **mean** when you **said** there's **no other townhouse** like **this** one in **all** of **New York City!** The **elevator stops** at **five floors**, yet it's **only** a **three-story building!** I just **hope** it's **big enough!** There's **plenty** of **room** for **me** to **ride** my **scooter**, but when **I'm** a **little older** and **get a car**, **driving around** in here **might** be a **little tight!**

ARTIST: RAY ALMA   WRITER: DICK DEBARTOLO

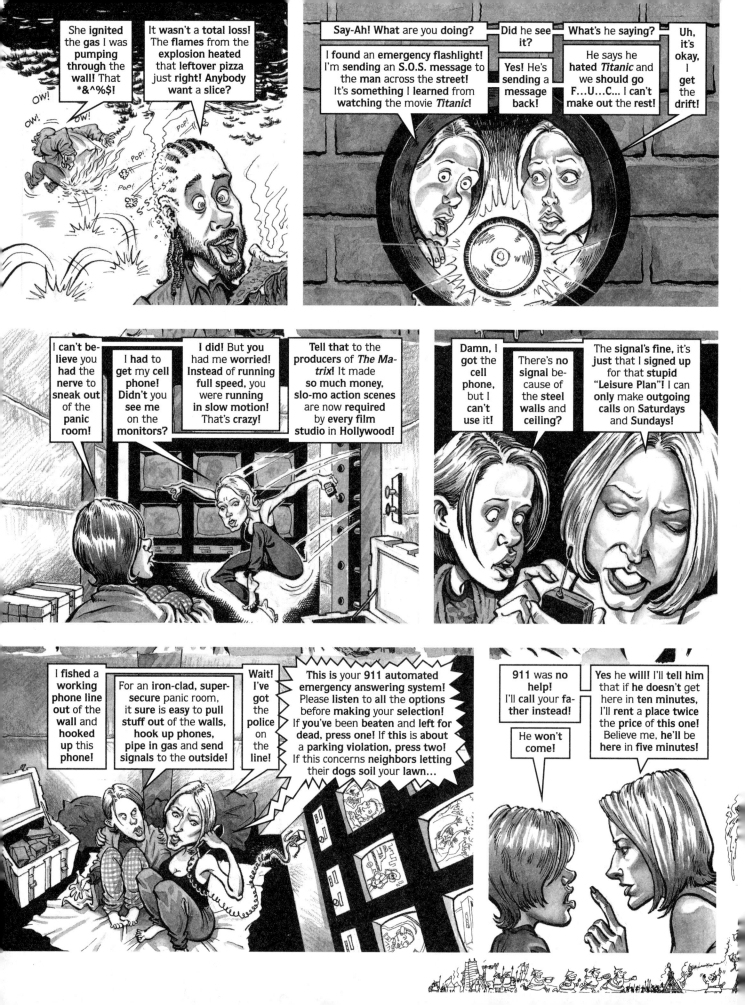

Mom, I'm **going** into a **coma!** Don't forget, I'm **suffering** from **BFMD —** Bad Formula Movie Disease! That **means** I'm **programmed** to **have** an **attack** at the most **inopportune** moment, like **now!**

Great! A **seizure** gives **me** a **chance** to do that **whole** "sneaking out of **here**" scene **again!** But **this time instead** of the cell phone, my **excuse is** so I can **get** your **medicine!** Obviously, Larry, **Moe** and **Curly** out there **won't** catch me **this time,** either!

BEEEEP!!

This **job** is **going down** the **drain!** We're **finally** in the **panic room** and the **kid** is **having** a **seizure!** Worse yet, her **mom's** out there **talking** to the **cops!**

If you **give me** my **shot,** my **mother** won't **give** you **away!**

Deal! But **only** if you have **medical coverage! Not only** will we **get what's** in the **safe,** but we **can make** a **bundle** by **overcharging** your **insurance company** for **giving** you the **shot,** just like real **doctors** do!

OW!

For a **state** of the **art panic room,** I would have **thought** they'd **install** something a little more **high-tech** than a **cheap, crappy, blinking** fluorescent light!

Be quiet! I **need** to **concentrate!** This **safe** has a **highly sophisticated locking** mechanism that… **huh?** The **safe's open!**

Oh, yeah! I **opened** it **with** a **bent paper clip!** I got **bored** in **here!**

BZZZT!

We **got** a **call** about **this house!** Seems **someone** from **here** sent out an **S.O.S.!** Did **this building** hit an **iceberg?**

No, **it's** been **clear sailing,** thanks!

Look lady, if **you're** in **trouble,** blink **three times!** If someone is **holding** a **gun** on **you, wiggle** your **ears five times!** If there's **more** than one **person** in there, **twitch** your **nose one time** for each **person!** If…

Look at **me!** I'm **yawning twice!**

Which means?

That you **two jokers** are **boring** me **out** of my **skull! Good night** already!

Your **daughter's fine** and I'm **leaving!**

What happened? Where are the **other two goons?**

Some guy **showed up** and **claimed** he was your **ex-husband!** He **thought** they were **real estate agents** and **shot** them both!

Aren't **those** the **papers** you **wanted** from the **safe?**

Yeah, **22 million dollars** in **bonds!**

Then **why** are **you throwing** them **to** the **wind?**

Turns out they're **Enron bonds!** They're **not even** worth **22 bucks!**

-SHAM TOO
Peeper Porker was supposed to meet me here, but I'm still waiting! Actually, it would be great if he showed up now! Maybe he'll get jealous if he sees me in the arms of another man, even *if* they're razor-sharp metal alloy arms!
DAILY ? BUNGLE
MAN BITES DOG
DOG SUES
MAX KORN ANNOUNCES BID FOR PRESIDENT
Spider-Sham's not doing a thing to help us! He must be in another one of his "split personality" quandaries! Anyone know how to get in touch with Superman? At least DC characters save lives with none of the angst!
Oh God, another crisis! What should I do? The more I follow my inner superhero instincts, the less I follow my outer "average Joe" instincts and the less I get to see my girlfriend, MT! And I want to see her more, not less! At least that's what I think…more or less!

Uncle Been, I can't live your dreams any more! I need a life of my own!

Peeper, you've been **given** a gift of **great power!** Do you **know** what **comes** along with **great power?**

A great pair of spandex tights?

Well, **yeah**, that's a **given!** But it **also** comes with a choice! To live your **own** life or the **life picked** for you by **your destiny!**

Is **that all** you can offer me — comic book hero rhetoric?

It's a lot **more** serious than that! It's a **pivotal plot** point, so don't take it lightly!

ETERNITY → 25 MI.

Hey did you **throw** this uniform in the garbage?

Yes, sir!

Well, **listen up!** Monday, you can **put out newspapers!** Wednesday, you can put out **metal** and **glass!** Friday, it's **plastic** and Saturday, it's discarded **superhero costume** day! **Today's Friday!** That's **gonna cost** you $25!

Big deal! I'll send them **five bucks** and my aunt's $20 I.O.U.!

LOST! AUDIENCE'S ATTENTION DURING THESE LONG, BORING, NO SPIDER-MAN SCENES! IF FOUND, CALL SAM RAIMI 555-PLOT

I have **big news** for you, MT! I've **changed** a lot in the **past two panels!** I **want** to be your **boyfriend again!**

Well I have **big news** for you too, Peeper! I'm **getting married!**

Oh, no! That changes every-thing, doesn't it?

Yes! We'll only be **able** to **date** when my **future husband** goes on busi-ness trips! But the **good news** is, since he's an as-tronaut, he **doesn't** just **leave town**, he **leaves Earth!** Pucker up!

I **found** this in the garbage!

Stop the presses! I want a new front page headline! "Spider-Sham Ends Career!" Then a **smaller** headline: "Sends publisher of *Daily Bungle* his Uniform As Proof He's Retired!"

Chief, how can you make up headlines that **aren't** true?

Easy, I trained at *The New York Post!*

KERRY'S CHOIC

I **can't believe** I'm **watching** a **mugging** and I'm **not lifting a fin-ger** to help!

Don't feel **bad!** You're **just** like the **other 200 people** watching and **not lifting a finger!**

I'm **not helping either!** These days, people are so **eager** to sue, it's **best not** to get involved!

Who **said** that?

I **did!**

I **have** a **confession, Aunt Mayday!** I just **can't live** with it any **more!**

Don't make such a **big deal** out of it, Peeper!

But I'm **afraid** it will **shock** you!

I'm a **modern woman!** I **know** a lot about **closet homosexuals!** I'm just **so glad** you decided **to come out!** Every time you **asked** me to sew a **button** on your **spandex tights**, I **knew!**

DAD?

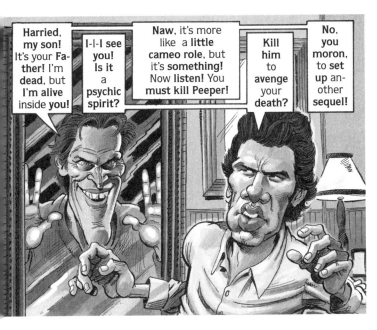

Plodder HAS GOTTA RETIRE

Harry Plodder! Herwhiny Grungy! Runt Queasy! I can still **remember** you the way you **children first** arrived here, **three DVDs ago**! What a **pleasure** it's been to watch you grow into a **fine young man** in Harry's case, or a **splendid young woman** in iss Grungy's. As for Runt Queasy, it could **still** go **either way**!

As **Headmistress**, I am very, **very** unhappy with all the **romance** going **on**, **in** and **around** my **Griddlecake House**! Mostly because I haven't **gotten any** since the **Dark Age**! Ah, what a **wonderful time** the Dark Age was. **Alas**, once the **lights** came **back on**, I was **out of luck**!

I'm jus' **so pleased** to be a **perfessor** here at Halfwits! I **couldn't** love my students **more** if they were **undulating gaseous gully frogs**! I don't know why I **identifies so strongly wit' abnormal** animals. I **wonder** about it every times I **combs** my **giant frizzled beard** or eat a gnu **raw**! I **needs** t' watch my **diet**, though. **I'm** th' **reason** these movies are filmed in **widescreen**! Right now I'm **1,608 pounds**, and that's *after* **six weeks** on the **South Witch Diet**!

For **years** now, I've had to sit back **jealously** and watch **other**, **less qualified** wizards **run the show**! I've had to put up with **abuse** from a sneaky, **wet-nosed** little **punk** who **never** seems to **lose**! Yes, I'm a **Democrat**. Why do you **ask**?

Yeah, yeah, **I know**, I could use an **extreme makeover**. It took a lot of **hard battles** and a slight **constipation problem** to turn me into "**Bad Eye Moonpie**"! Hey, at least my **right eyeball** is **normal**, which puts me **one up** on **Ashley Olsen**! I was **glad** to take the vacant **Defense Against Dork Arts** teaching position, not so much for the **salary** as for the **health benefits**. I go through about **three gallons** of **Visine** a day!

Harry Plodder, you've **beaten** me **time and again**. But I wouldn't be **Lord Druckermort** if I didn't have a good **backup backup backup backup plan**! Right now, though, I need to **lie down** and **rest** for a **year or so**. My body is in **ruins** and I need to have my **arm** replaced. On the **plus** side, I've been offered a **slot** in the New York Yankees' **starting rotation**!

Master, it is an **honor** to serve you! I am happy to **grovel** in your **magnificent shadow**, shamelessly **overeager** to fulfill your **smallest command**. I'm even thinking of changing my name to "**Condoleezza**"! The **ultimate reward** for my **loyalty** will be when you **rise again** and make me your **right hand man**. Er, make that **left** hand!

On **second** thought, I'm thinking of **transferring** to a **home-schooling** system at the **Neverland Ranch**! It's a much **safer** environment for **confused young boys**!

The **Squamish Cup championship** is a million times **faster** and more **violent** than the games you're used to at **Halfwits**. But it's getting way too **overcommercialized**...

Pow! Young superstar **Virile Skum** has just **dislocated** Adam Cooke's **elbow**. Cooke is in **agony**...and fans, if **you've** been **dislocated**, why not rent a U-Haul? Play continues, and here comes **Ireland's** trio of **chasers**. Like a heaping bowl of frosted **Lucky Charms**, these Irish speedsters are **magically delicious**. Oh, no! There's been some kind of **enchanted explosion**. The players are **horribly burned**! The **flesh** is **melting** off their **limbs** and **faces**!

Yes, but I have some **good news**. I just **saved** a bunch of **money** on my **broom insurance**!

Welcome to another **thrill-packed semester** here at **Halfwits**! Together, we shall **accomplish** the **impossible**! Namely, take a **734-page book** and somehow **cram** it into a **130-minute movie**! So if you're into those **annoying chapters** with the "civil rights movement for elves," take your **geeky nerd diatribes** to the **internet**! That **subplot** is OUT of here!

As **headmaster** here at **Halfwits**, I am entrusted with **protecting** the **safety** of every student. On the other hand, **what the heck**! Thus I happily announce the **resumption** of the **deadly, once-banned Toowitless Tournament**! Three schools shall **compete**! Any **Halfwits student** over the age of **17** may enter their **name** for the enviable **privilege** of being **incinerated, drowned** or **squished**! It's **no wonder** our school's **passing rate** is **95%**, but its **survival rate** is **82%**!

The "oompahpah" **spell** makes these spiders **twitch**! The "ralphmacchio" **spell** makes 'em **bleed**! And the illegal "gabbagabbahey" **spell** sucks the **life** right out of them!

Can we use these **spells** against **Lord Druckermort**?

Who cares? I just think **torturing bugs** is **FUN**!

It's the **two schools** that put the "**rival**" in "**arrival**"! The all-boys school **Spermgang** has already marched in. And now, say hello to the all-girls school, **Babeathon**! Everyone's so **thrilled** to see their **magnificent carriages** soaring **overhead**!

Except the **unlucky ones**... right **under** the **horses**!

And the **three contestants** will be... from Spermgang, **Virile Skum**! From Babeathon, **Fleur Dexatrim**! And from Halfwits, **Eccentric Buggery**! Wait! There's a **fourth** — Harry Plodder! **Shocking!** Who could have **imagined** this, except **anyone** who saw the **small clue** hidden in the **movie's title**?

Sorry, Harry. It's against the **rules** and incredibly **dangerous**. Yes, and Druckermort is trying to **kill you**. But there's **no way out**. The metal cup says you **have to play!**

Harry Plodder! Harry Plodder! **Banana Fana Fo Fodder!** Just because you're **pure** and **brave** and **good** and **loyal**, you think you're **so great**! Well, I'm **sick** of living in your **shadow**! Admittedly, shadows are **good** for my **pasty British skin**...

Let him **vent**. It's **hard** for **Runt** to be your personal **Nicole Richie!**

That's okay. In **every movie**, this is where the **whole school** turns **against** me for **no reason**. It's so **predictable**, they list my **annual ostracization** in the Halfwits **course catalogue!**

Rita Skeever here for **Faux News**. Harry Plodder, why are you **soft** on **terrorism**? Do you **repudiate** the blame game? Will you be **helping** a heartbroken **Jennifer Aniston** to **pick up** the pieces? I'll give you the **last word**. But **before I do**, you might like to **know** that the **response** to our unscientific online **Harry Plodder** poll was "**33 percent.**"

You mean they think I have a **1-in-3 chance** of **winning** the **Toowitless Tournament?**

Not quite. After you get **roasted alive**, there'll only be about a **third** of you left to **bury!**

I have a **big problem**. I used my **invisibility cloak** to follow **Haggard** and **Madame Maximum** into the **woods** and saw the **first Toowitless challenge**. A **dragon!**

I'd say your **biggest problem** is that you're using that **cloak** to watch **Haggard** instead of spying on **girls**! Whoops, **gotta go**! I'm on **Sprint**, and their **roaming charges** on **person-to-fireplace calls** are through the **roof!**

Behold! Only **one** shall go down in **history**! Only **one** wins **eternal glory** in a **legendary tournament** no one ever **heard** of until a **few weeks** ago! Is anybody **buying** this? **Anyone?** Is this **mic** on? **Testing, testing!**

ERADICATE & SCORCH POTTER'S NADS!

Harry Plodder is one of the **400 bravest people** I've ever **known!**

400? Who are the other **399?**

All of us **here** in the **stadium**! If that **dragon** decides to **turn** his **head** and **cough**, we're **toast**! **Literally!**

HAT WOULD DUMBLEDORK DO?

We need a couple of **dates** for the **Christmas dance**. Fortunately, I have a **plan**. I'm going to keep **stalking Cha Ching** around the **hallway corridors**, giving her **steamy blank looks**. From what I **know** about **girls**, they just **LOVE** that! How about **you?**

I **finally** worked up the **courage** to speak with **Fleur Dexatrim**. Of course, she's **French**, so we didn't quite **communicate**. What does "**stuffez-vous, le dorke**" mean?

DISGRACER

Which are the most richly textured and emotionally rewarding — the "very special" episodes of *Step By Step,* or the regular old kind? — IT'S A MOOT POINT.

Thank Gondor, it's finally over! The first war trilogy that went on longer than the actual war! Why? So that nine hours of digital noodling and countless l-l-o-o-o-n-n-n-g-g "meaningful" gazes can be dumped into the DVD along with that damned "aaaaaahhh-aaaaaahhhh" soundtrack from the castrato choir of the Role Players Church! The problem is, we GOT it already! Everything this movie has to say, it said way back in the first "Fellowship" movie! Next came the jog-in-place "Two Towers," in which not a single character got two inches closer to his goal! It's obvious, we're all...

BORED OF THE RINGS

REHASH OF THE THING

ARTIST: HERMANN MEJIA   WRITER: DESMOND DEVLIN

...ined by my **friends**, I'm on a **quest** to claim my **rightful** ...one and be **reunited** with my ...ue love! Why do I suddenly ...ve the urge to sing "**Hakuna** ...tata"? The crown has passed ...n such legends as **Elendil the** ...II, **Valandil the Faithful**, and **Isildur the Swift**. ...nd now, me — **Peppercorn** ...e Unwashed and Unshaven!

I'm **Legolamb**, the only **action hero** ever to get called "**sissypants**" by **Clay Aiken**! A lot of **purists** don't like the way I've become some kind of **Xtreme skateboard warrior** onscreen! But there's not a **single moment** that isn't **100%** in keeping with the **original Tolkien books**. "**Respect the work**" is my **motto**. Now **scope** me while I **railslide** into a **totally sick crooked grind**, and **acid drop** that **dorc's butt**!

I'm **3-foot-4** and I carry a **2-foot sword**. Think I've got any **psychological issues** to **work out**? In the **original books**, I'm the **dignified representative** of a **dying race**. In these **movies**, I've been **dumbed down** to a "**Tickle Me Gimmicki**" who cracks **corny jokes**. But it's tough to maintain **artistic vision** when your **sightline** is right at **half a million butts** all the time!

That's where you're **wrong**, **Gimmicki!** As the **director** of these films, I don't consider a **short**, **fat**, **hairy little troll** to be the **comic relief!** To **me**, you're the **sex symbol!**

The **soldiers** say, "**Baggybuns**, you're **too small** to join us in **hand-to-hand combat**!" But they're **wrong**! I survived **several years** working as an **alter boy**!

Fear not, **Baggybuns!** I shall **carry you** astride my **horse** as we **ride** into **battle**! Hey, **I'm no fool!** As long as I've got **you** sitting **up front**, you **block 80%** of the **arrows** coming at **me**!

As the **king**, if I'm going to send my **army** to get **killed**, it would be **ungallant** for me to **hide** in my **safe palace**! A **true leader** must **take up** the **sword** and place himself in the same **mortal danger** as his **own people**! Now **THAT'S** why this story is a **total fantasy**!

I'm **proud** to be a part of what **many critics** consider a **mature masterpiece** of **storytelling**! I play **Pimple**, a **midget** who finds a **magic ball** in the **water** next to a **talking tree**, which lets the **giant evil eyeball fry** my **brain**. **Proud?** Um...on **second thought**, I think I'll tell my **children** that **Daddy** works in **gay porn**!

All we have to **eat** is this **tasteless dry bread**, which is **crawling** with **teeny mealygrubs** and **wrapped** in **dirty leaves**. Here, **you** can take **mine!**

What a **pal!** What a **pal!**

Yum! **Fishes** are much **tastier** thans **slobbit bread!** Yeah, and **we** gets **seconds!** You **fat pig**, it's like **you're eating** for **two!** Forgets the **fish**, let's talk about our **Precious!** We must **gets** our **Preciousss! Shhh!** Do you **thinkings** maybe we should **move** this **conversation** more than **ten feet away** from the **slobbits?** Nah! What are the **chances** that somebody with **gigantic ears** could possibly **overhears** us?

Poor **Cheese-ball**. I've **never seen** a **creature** like **him!**

Me neither! But his **schizophrenic baby** talk does **remind** me a lot of **Michael Jackson** trying to **explain** what **went on** out at **Neverland Ranch!**

Where's **Aspercreme?**

Where's **who?** Oh, you mean the **super-evil wizard** who created the **army** to **destroy us?** The one who almost **killed Gandoof?** Um, he's up in the **tower**. Yeah. Up **there. That's** where **he** is!

Doesn't it strike **anyone** as odd that the **final fate** of the **#1 villain** in these **movies** gets totally **blown off** with an obviously **patched-in** line of **exposition?**

Not to me, it doesn't! We've got **$35 DVDs** to sell! And **that's** why we shoot a **dozen extra scenes** for the **completist fanboy suckers** — I mean, **lovers** of **cinema** — to **drool over!** So if you want to see what I like to call **"the lost Aspercreme sequence,"** be sure to **preorder now!**

You must **relinquish** the **throne!** You are **merely** the **caretaker king!** You were **never** actually **chosen** to be the **true leader!**

Yeah, but **five-ninths** of the Middle-earth **Supreme Court** picked me, so **nyah-nyah-nyah! $300 tax cuts** for **everybody! Mission accomplished!**

I am the **Witch-King of Angrymaw!** Some know me as the **Lord of the Fazool!** Still **others** speak of the **Greatest of the Nine!** But **you** can call me **N. Diddy!** Now, **follow** me to the **city of men!**

It's **un-believable! 200,000 dorcs** marching into **battle!**

What's **really un-believable** is that **not one** of these **hammerheads** happens to **glance** to his **right** and **spot us!**

We've lost **half** our **army!** The **invaders** are **here!** The **city** is **lost!**

Hmmm! Maybe that **"letting them all run past us" strategy** wasn't as **sharp** as we **originally thought!**

Gyaahh!! That horrible, high-pitched **dragon shriek!** I haven't **heard anything** like it since I caught **Celine Dion's** Vegas show!

Gandoof! How did you **know** that you could **chase away** the **dragons** with a **beam** of light?

My **hut** has **cockroaches!** Every time I flick the **lights on** in the **kitchen,** they **go running!** If it works on **them,** I figure it **could work on dragons!**

I've put my **son's life** in **mortal danger,** just like **Steve Irwin** the Crocodile Hunter! My **phony-baloney kingdom** is **collapsing!** Come, **Pimple,** sing a **soothing song** to **distract** me!

My milkshake...
*brings all the **boys** to the **yard,***
*And **they're** like...*
*"It's **better** than **yours.**"*
Damn right,** it's **better** than **yours.
*I can **teach** you,*
*but I **have** to **charge.***

Well, I have to **admit,** that **certainly** took my **mind off things!**

Master Dodo, you're **listening** to **Cheeseball,** and ordering **me** to leave?

Yes, I've decided to **trust** the **crazy-eyed, schizophrenic, bald-headed little freak** over **you,** my **oldest** and **dearest friend.** It makes **perfect sense!**

You mean I'm not **allowed** to **climb** straight up a **sulphurous black mountain** anymore? I have to **go home?** And **eat** some **real food?** And **sleep** in a **bed?** Hee hee! Oh, um, **that** was a **giggle** of **sadness!**

The **horses** are **restless** tonight!

There are **half a million lonely soldiers** in this **movie** and just **three girls!** The **horses SHOULD** be **restless!**

Here, **Peppercorn!** The **Sword of Advil** has been **reforged.** You can use **this** to **summon** the **armies** of the **dead.** Have you any **questions?**

Yeah, a **big one!** **Why** didn't you just **tell me** the **exact same thing,** way back in the **first movie?** Nailhead!

This is a **fight** we **cannot win!** We face **overpowering odds! Certain doom!** And yet, we shall **meet** them in **battle,** nonetheless! And do you **know** what **men** shall **call us?**

Yes! Democrats!

The upside-down kiss with **Spider-Sham** — that used to be our kiss!

If you feel be-**trayed**, MT, you have to **express yourself!** It's **not healthy to seethe** inwardly!

You're right! I think I'm going to **sing** "The **Man** Who **Got Away**"!

On the **other hand,** there's a **lot** to be said for **seething** in-wardly!

Hello, **escaped convict!**

I really don't want to **fight** you, **Spider-Sham!** I have **no stomach** for this!

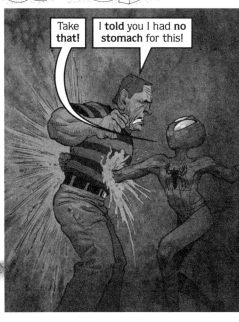

Take **that!**

I **told** you I had **no stomach** for this!

Hey, **what's happening?!** Something **creepy crawly** is **all over me!** It could be the **landlord's daughter!** No, it's something even **ickier!** Hey, it feels **good!** I feel **different!** I feel **stronger!** I'm becoming **someone else!** I'm changing into...

...the **exact same guy,** only in a **different costume!**

Actually, I'm **darker, moodier, creepier!** It's like I've got an **evil twin!** Now I've got **two personalities!**

Incidentally, **neither** of them **thrilling!**

Why me, Spider-Sham? **Why** are you after **me?**

This time it's **personal, Blandman!** I discovered **you** killed my beloved **Uncle Ben!**

I committed those **crimes** to raise **money** to help an **ailing daughter!**

I **feel** your **pain** — now **feel mine!**

I've **never** seen **this** before!

A **convict's face** pressed against a **train** and **dissolving** into **sand!?**

Actually, **violence, freakos** and **weird stuff** I see all the time! A **NYC subway train** on schedule... **THAT** I've **never** seen before!

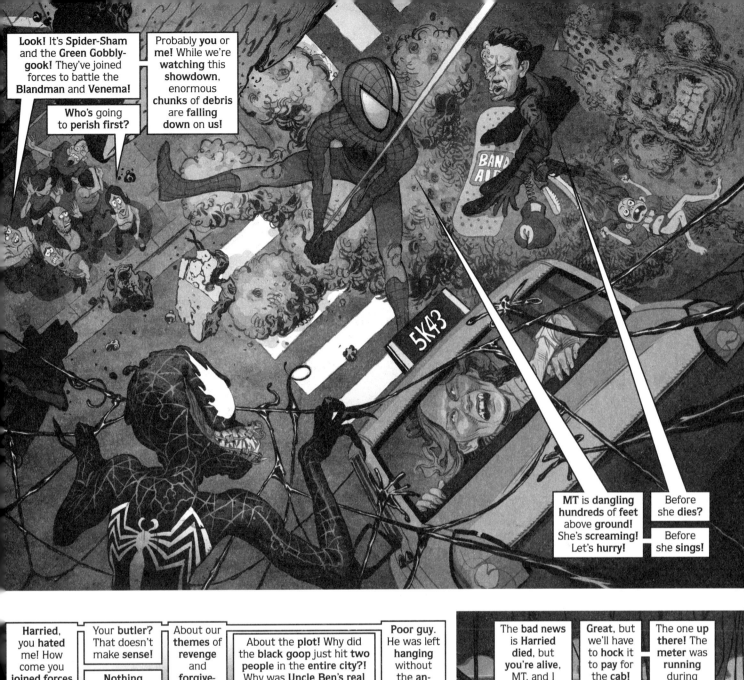

As everybody in the universe knows, J.K. Rowling's wizard story comes in seven parts. In the first book, Voldemort tries to kill Harry. In the second book, Voldemort tries to kill Harry. In the third, Rowling shakes up the formula in a major way: Voldemort's HELPER tries to kill Harry. Book #4? Zap, we're right back to Voldemort trying to kill Harry. And now it's time for the big-screen version of Book #5. Although we don't want to give away any of the surprises, let's just say that a certain Mr. V has some nasty plans for our hero. Come ON, already! We're dying to see SOMEthing, ANYTHING, that's even a little bit different! But this drip-drip-drip formula is just...

Haggard's gone and they've replaced him with a centaur! Professor McConjugal was attacked and sent to the hospital! Doubledork has disappeared!

The Queasy twins have just quit school! Druckermort has almost captured the ultimate weapon!

Everything's happening too fast!

Hey, YOU try cramming 869 pages of book into a lousy two-hour movie! That whole subplot about Haggard's giant half-brother Grawp can only be glimpsed briefly in the reflection of my eyeglasses!

Brrr! Another nightmare about Seriously Wacked being tortured by Druckermort in a room of spheres! I've got to contact Seriously somehow! Should I use the two-way magic mirror that's right next to my bed? Nah! Instead, I think I'll try breaking and entering into the private office of my #1 enemy at Halfwits! It's foolproof! And I'm just the fool who'll prove it!

Harry's picking up Seriously Wacked's trail like a homing pigeon, and he's making a beeline for the Ministry! He's got to stop Druckermort the snake from killing Seriously the dog! And we're coming along, like a bunch of prize jackasses!

I can feel it! We need to walk down THIS hallway! Just like in my snake dream!

You didn't happen to dream the location of the loo, did you? Because all this suspense has my bladder ready to blow!

Yikes! Five of Lord Druckermort's personal Death Eaters!

Actually, I'm more of a Death Snacker! Eating Death always goes right to my hips!

Come one step closer, and I'll smash it! I'll destroy the crucial sphere!

The prophecy contained in that sphere reveals how we will kill you! So tell us how we'll kill you, or else we'll kill you!

Why couldn't you just pick up the sphere and read it yourself?

Oh, NOW you're asking for logic in these stories? If Druckermort could visit the inside of your head and read your thoughts, why did he wait four years to do it? If we needed you to enter the sphere room for us, so that we wouldn't get caught breaking into the Ministry, why did we just break in anyway? Why could you go back in time to restore the life of a stupid eagle-horse two movies ago, but anyone killed in this movie has to stay dead? THINK, Plodder! Without arbitrary plot devices, you'd have been snuffed in your crib!

My **son**, I want to give **you** the same thing **my** father gave me when **I** was **seven** years old!

And **what** is **that**, my father? Wisdom? Skill?

Internal bleeding!

Once I pay the **corrupt priests** their **bribe money**, I hope they'll give their **official blessing** to my **war plans**! On **second thought**, how the **hell** will anybody **know** what those **creepy freaks** have to say about **anything**, from the top of this **inaccessible mountain**? I should just **climb back down** and **tell everybody** they totally **loved** my **plan**!

SIN CITY
NEW YORK
OZ

Treachery! The **Persians** will **slash** our **intestines** out! They'll **tear** our **eyes** from our **heads**! They'll **whip** our **children bloody**, and take our **women** on top of a **mountain** of **Spartan corpses**!

Oh, **baby**, baby! You **really know** how to **sweet-talk** a **girl**!

Look at the **300**! **300 magnificent specimens**! They are Sparta's **300 finest soldiers**!

More **importantly**, **300** is their collective **I.Q.**! **Nobody** with a **brain** would ever **volunteer** for this **hopeless suicide mission**!

I shall **remember** our **marital passion**!

Yeah, great. It was the **only thing** in this **movie** that DOESN'T play out in extreme slow motion!

THERE IS NO PLACE FOR **SOFTNESS** IN SPARTA. **SPARTA** IS A **HARD PLACE.** NOT **SOFT.** ARE YOU THINKING IT MIGHT BE **SOFT?** WELL, YOU'RE **WRONG.** ITS **HARDITY** IS — HEY, **ZACK,** DIDN'T I **READ** THIS PART **ALREADY?** IS **ANYBODY** EVEN **CHECKING** THIS **COPY?**

Our **battle strategy** is **sophisticated** and **complex**! Can you **explain** the **details** to the **troops**, Mentos?

Yes! Jab 'em with the **pointed side** of the **stick**, and make the **red stuff** go **spurty-spurty**!

Well done! In Sparta, that kind of **critical thinking** qualifies you as **officer material**!

No, **valiant lump**, you may **NOT** join us in **battle**! Your **ugly**, **misshapen** body is an **affront** to the **Greek god** that all **Spartan** men **worship**!

Which god? Is it **Tartarus**? **Artemis**?

Nautilus!

We're **outnumbered** by **3,500** to **1**! But we can use the **narrow passageway** here as a **natural defensive position**! It's a **foolproof plan**!

But won't we **eventually** get **slaughtered**?

Okay, so there's a **catch**! But consider **this**: if we do not **stop** the **Persians**, their **armies** of **vicious warriors** shall **sweep** across the **land**, **killing** without **mercy** and **creating** a **culture** of **blood** and **fear**! Any **questions**?

Yes! How will **anyone** be able to **tell** the **difference**?

I DON'T WANT TO FIGHT NO MORE

I'm **confused**! Why do you **Spartans** make such a **big deal** about **holding position** in tightly packed **battle formations**, and then let your best soldiers **spin around** on their **own**, in **slow motion**, with **no protection** whatsoever?

Try **huddling** under **heavy shields** with a **dozen** greasy, sweaty, meaty **guys**! We **Spartans** are known for **cruelty** and **courage**! *Hygiene's* another matter! I'll take my **chances** out **here**!

Let's **show 'em**, boys! **Nobody** messes with the **Persian Airborne Division**!

But **airplanes** haven't been **invented** yet!

Aw, **crap!**

Sire, there's a fully **shaved**, flamingly **effeminate**, topless **bald black man** with **piercings** to **see** you...

I've **never met** any... that is, **what** the **heck** could he **possibly** wish to **speak privately** about... I **mean**, I **don't** even **know** the **guy**!

He's at least **eight feet tall**, too!

Oh, **EIGHT** feet? **Phew!** Well, **what** do you **know**? I really **DON'T know** the guy!

We've killed all **99,999** of them! **Nothing** can possibly go **wrong** now!

That's **my son!** A real **chip** off the old block... oops!

YOU MAY HAVE *NOTICED* A SLIGHT, SUBLIMINAL *GAY UNDERTONE* TO THE PROCEEDINGS! AW, WHO AM *I* TRYING TO *FOOL?* THIS *MAN-TASTIC CAST* HAS GOT ENOUGH *GAY TENSION* TO CHOKE A *PERSIAN RHINOCEROS!* BUT SINCE WE *CAN'T* TAKE THE *FINAL, LOGICAL STEP* IN A *MAINSTREAM MOVIE, THIS* HAS TO BE OUR *"MONEY SHOT"!*

Here, within my travelling **sex tent**, you will **immerse** yourself in a **succulent miasma** of **erotic pleasures** of the flesh! Some of the **techniques** you shall **experience** are so **depraved** that they do not have a **name!** And **all** you must do to **join** the undulating **orgy** is betray a **King** who does not **honor** your **service!**

You **had** me at "**sex tent**"! It's a **deal**! **Tie up** those disfigured **lesbian triplets** into a **naked hexagon**! I'll be back in **five minutes** with a **whip**, a wooden **ox cart**, and this **bouquet** of **flowers!**

A bouquet of **flowers?**

Just call me **old-fashioned!**

SPARTAN SOLDIERS ARE *TRAINED* WELL. NO *MERCY.* NO *RETREAT.* NO *SURRENDER.* AND NOT MUCH OF A *TURNOUT* AT THE *VETERANS DAY PARADES!*

The **hunchback** has **betrayed** you, my **King!** He **revealed** the **hidden pathway** to the Persians!

Damn! That's what I get for **building** a **handicapped ramp!** Say! What was that **thud?**

It was my **son's** decapitated **head, finally** hitting the **ground!** Now THAT'S what I call a **slow motion death scene!**

PLOP!

My **message** to the **council** is a single word...**freedom!** Or two words, **free** and **dumb!** In Sparta, freedom isn't **free!** But it sure is **dumb! Now** is the **hour** you must **stand up** for **justice**, and **honor** and **freedom!** For only through **freedom** can **free** men be **free!** You know, maybe I should have **prepared** more than **one index card!**

With your **talk** of **freedom**, does this mean you're going to **quit** being **Queen**, and **establish** a **Spartan representative government?**

Whoa, there! Now let's **not** have any **crazy talk!**

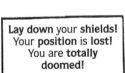

Lay down your **shields!** Your **position** is lost! You are **totally doomed!**

I **disagree!** It's just that the **liberal media** won't **report** the **good news** from our **massacre!**

AND *THUS* DID THE *300* FIGHT! AND *THUS* DID THE *300* DIE! TODAY, ON THE *EVE OF WAR,* WE *REMEMBER* THEIR *FATE!* WE *REMEMBER* HOW THEY WERE *BRAVELY CUT APART* WITH *SWORDS*, AND *GLORIOUSLY PUNCTURED* WITH *ARROWS*, AND *HEROICALLY GURGLED* THEIR OWN *BLOOD!* THEIR *BRUTALLY PAINFUL DEATH* IN-SPIRES *FREE MEN* TO *MARCH FORWARD,* HEADS HELD *HIGH,* AND...

HEY! WHERE DID *EVERYBODY GO?*

VAMPIRE

ARTIST: MORT DRUCKER   WRITER: STAN HART

Not for the **way I make** a Bloody Mary!

ARE YOU ONE OF US?

ELEANOR?

Not if it was **Tom Cruise** they showed in **frontal nudity!** Then, they would have **grossed** more than **Jurassic Park!**

I'm a **reporter** for a **super-market tabloid!** I understand **you're** the **ghost** of Elvis!

I never said **that!**

Then you **must be** one of the **people** who were **kidnapped** by **creatures** from a U.F.O.!

Nope!

Well, you're not **Siamese twins** — so, unless you have **another leg** or **arm** you're **hiding,** I doubt **anything** you have **to** say would **interest** our **readers!**

I'm a **vampire!**

Just **what** does **that mean?**

Although I am of **flesh** and **blood,** I have **no human** feelings or emotions!

You're the **second person** like that I've **interviewed** this **week!** The other was **Newt Gingrich!**

Just how old are you, Loser?

I was born in the mid-1750s!

Aren't there a lot of problems with being that old?

Indeed there are! You can't imagine how many ugly ties and sweaters a person can accumulate by having over 200 birthdays!

My wife and daughter had died and I was despondent! I no longer had any desire to live and wanted to end my life! Then I met him — Le Fotostat!

I am Le Fotostat, a vampire! If I bite you and you drink my blood, you will also become a vampire! You will have eternal life!

Why would I want to live forever if I just said I wanted to die?

You'll get used to it!

To living?

No! To the inconsistencies that run through this entire movie!

I start by biting your neck...

Hmmm, I don't know...

Just think of it as a hickey with an attitude!

Sleeping in a coffin has its drawbacks! I can't imagine any woman would want to go to bed with me in here!

Your puppy dog "jammies" don't help a lot, either!

SPECIAL: CHICKEN IN A CASKET

Why are you biting the neck of that actress?

I call it "Dinner Theater"!

Since you refuse to drink human blood, you'll have to exist on the blood of animals! Here's a nice juicy rat for you!

Yecch! That's absolutely disgusting!

Well, there's an up side and a down side! The up side is that they're never out of season! The down side is that once you start, you can't eat just one!

PLOP! PLOP! PLOP!

I knew you would find my story interesting!

As the years went by, I had many questions! One: wouldn't we be damned for our actions? And two: what did Le Fotostat do for a living?

BARRFFOOOO

DEVILED HAM AND SCRAMBLED LEGS DEPT.

Every once in a while, a new movie comes along that's funny, clever and in good taste. Maybe one day we'll be lucky enough to see one! Until then, we'll just have to take whatever Hollywood throws up to us as we try to stomach...

THE WRETCHES OF ECCHFLICK

Operator, we're **three girls alone** in this **big house** and we just got an **obscene call!** Of **course** this is a **complaint!** We were **cut off** in the middle of a **heavy breath!** Can you please **trace it** and **re-connect** us?

Boy, that **gets me mad** when we get **disconnected!**

Well, look at the **bright side.** At least our **toll-free 800 number** is starting to **pay off!** I get to answer the **next one!**

How about if we use our **occult powers,** invoke a **mystical spell** and create a **Galahad** or a **Prince Charming?**

No one will **believe it!**

That we can really **do it?**

No, that three **babes** with our **bodies** and **looks** are **hard up** for **dates** on a **Saturday night!**

ARTIST: MORT DRUCKER   **WRITER: FRANK JACOBS**

Obsessia, I just heard a **mysterious stranger** bought the **Lummox Mansion!**

NO, NOT THAT! OUR LIVES WILL BE RUINED! OUR TOWN WILL BE DESTROYED! WE'RE HEADED STRAIGHT FOR HELL!

She really seems **upset!** She's **shouting** in capital letters!

You should have heard her when the **gay bar** opened! She **screamed** in italics!

Some **perfect man** we've created! He's **gross, slobbering** and **drunk!** Are we that **stupid?**

No—that **desperate!** Just **listening** to him is **revolting!**

To **us** it's **revolting!** To **him** it's **foreplay!**

Braf...zlug...snore... zlotch...gurgle...yulk!

You're **disgusting,** yet I feel **drawn** to you! **Why?**

Because I can **look** into your **soul!** I can see how you've been **held back** by **lesser mortals** who've **prevented** you from being a **complete woman!**

Then you **know** about Sonny Bono!

ISHTAR

THANK YOU FOR CHER-IN

Let's **undress!** What would you like me to **take off** first?

Looking at your **body,** how about **twenty years?**

SATAN SHEETS

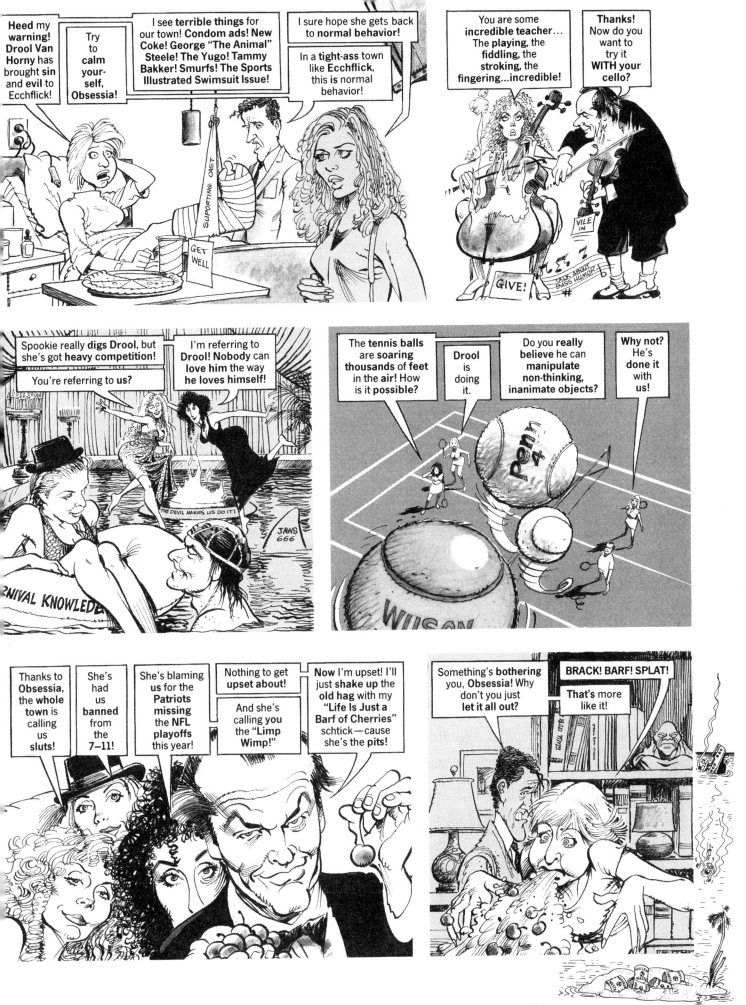

Clod just **killed** Obsessia, and you made it happen, **Drool!** How did you get your **evil insane power?**

Through **reincarnation!** In my **first** life I was a **hopeless drunk** in "Easy Rider"! Then I **reincarnated** as a **radical weirdo** in "Five Easy Pieces," was **reborn** as a **nut case** in "One Flew Over the Cuckoo's Nest" and came back again as a **homicidal maniac** in "The Shining"!

Why is Spookie bent over in pain?

Because **Drool** is sending **destructive impulses** through the **atmosphere** to her **body!**

Gee, if he had only sent them by the **U.S. Postal Service**— she **never** would have **received them!**

I'm **sorry** but we can't **help her.** She doesn't have the "mysticism curse" rider in her **Blue Cross** policy...

We created **Drool!** Now we must **destroy him** by using this **voodoo doll!** I'll stick a pin in his **leg** to cause **incredible pain...**

And I'll **stick a pin** in his **arm** to cause **even more pain.** What are you going to do, Abracadabra?

Let me think... Hmmm— I have this **electric pencil sharpener...**

We'll **jab** him until he **screams in pain!**

Make him **vomit** until he **coughs up a major organ**—and moviegoers cough up their **Goobers!**

When I said "Give from way down deep," this **isn't exactly** what I had in mind!

Something tells me there was **something wrong** with those **cherry pies** I made for the **church bake sale!**

I got that **yucky stuff** over **half** my face!

The **worst part** is the **Bible** says we gotta **turn the other cheek!**

BARF FLY

...And finally **obliterate him!**

BLAM!

Drool's back in the **supernatural world** and each of us has his **child!** Do you think people will **know** he was the **father?** After all, the babies **do look like Drool!**

And **sound** just like **Drool!**

And **especially...**

THROW UP LIKE DROOL!!

FROM THE MOUTHS OF BABES

Barf!

Bleeah!

Braack!

A nine year old boy sees ghosts everywhere he looks. That's pretty spooky! For help, he turns to a child psychologist played by Bruce Willis. That's even spookier! It shows the kid has...

THE SICK SENSE

ARTIST: ANGELO TORRES   WRITER: DICK DEBARTOLO

I'm **Doctor Malcoma Croup,** gifted **child psychologist!** As you can see by my half-hearted **smirk,** I'm particularly good at **conning childr**— er, at **TREATING** children with **psychological problems!** What a doctor **fears most** is when those children grow up to become **adults,** and realize **my treatment failed** them — as evidenced by the **semi-nude, deranged** former patient holding a **gun** on me and my **wife!** I'd offer to **help him,** but I don't accept his **HMO plan!** Tough break for him!

Remember me, Doc!? I tried to commit **suicide** by **jumping** out a third story window, **slitting** my wrists, **hanging** myself and **swallow-ing** poison! You classified me as "a bit **moody,**" and "**not very good** at **completing tasks**"! Well, I **completed something** today, Doc! I found out where you **lived,** and I broke into your **home!** And I just **completed undressing!**

Please **put down** that **gun!** You're not giving my husband very much **credit** for his **outstanding work!** In all the years he's been treating people, not once did he have the **luxury** of a **totally-adjusted, well-balanced person** coming to him to seek treatment! Don't you think it wears on a **psychologist,** when only **mentally deranged** people like you — you friggin' **nutjob** — come to him for help!? Look, we've just **finished** an expensive **bottle** of **wine** to celebrate an **important award** my husband won! And now we're about to **make love!** So can you **put down** the **gun** for **30 seconds** till he's **finished?**

I'm **Mrs. Seer!** There's something very **strange** about my son, Cold! Sometimes he seems to talk to **invisible people,** and when he does, the **temperature** in the house **plummets** and it gets as **cold** as a **morgue!** Sure, I wish he could be more **normal,** but on the other hand we save a **fortune** on **air conditioning!**

So that's the **new doctor** who's going to **help me!** He seems kind of **animated!** At least he seems animated when you **compare him** to the people I talk to most: **dead people!**

I'm the **family dog!** No one **walks** me or **plays** with me! And it's been **so long** since they **fed** me, I'm about to become a **dead dog,** which won't be so bad! At least once I'm **dead,** Cold will **pay more attention** to me!

A MAD LOOK AT MOVIE MAKING

ARTIST AND WRITER: SERGIO ARAGONES